BIG BOOK
OF
MATH
PRACTICE PROBLEMS

Addition & Subtraction

by

Stacy Otillio & Frank Otillio

EMPOWERING CHILDREN
FOR A SUCCESSFUL FUTURE

TABLE OF CONTENTS

TABLE OF CONTENTS

SECTION

ADDITION FACTS

11 worksheets
20 problems per sheet

Addition Facts

Add.

1)   1
   + 5
   ___
    6

2)   6
   + 2
   ___
    9

3)   2
   + 9
   ___
    11

4)   4
   + 2
   ___
    6

5)   7
   + 4
   ___
    11

6)   1
   + 3
   ___
    4

7)   5
   + 2
   ___
    7

8)   2
   + 4
   ___
    6

9)   8
   + 2
   ___
    10

10)   7
    + 2
    ___
     9

11)   3
    + 6
    ___
     9

12)   1
    + 6
    ___
     7

13)   2
    + 5
    ___
     7

14)   1
    + 1
    ___
     2

15)   6
    + 8
    ___
     14

16)   3
    + 2
    ___
     5

17)   6
    + 7
    ___
     13

18)   7
    + 9
    ___
     16

19)   7
    + 7
    ___
     14

20)   9
    + 9
    ___
     18

Addition Facts

Add.

1) 6
  + 2
  —
  8

2) 4
  + 2
  —
  6

3) 9
  + 3
  —
  12

4) 4
  + 7
  —
  11

5) 2
  + 4
  —
  6

6) 5
  + 5
  —
  10

7) 5
  + 9
  —
  14

8) 5
  + 8
  —
  13

9) 9
  + 4
  —
  13

10) 5
  + 4
  —
  9

11) 3
  + 7
  —
  10

12) 7
  + 7
  —
  14

13) 1
  + 8
  —
  9

14) 5
  + 3
  —
  8

15) 7
  + 8
  —
  15

16) 8
  + 9
  —
  17

17) 6
  + 9
  —
  15

18) 9
  + 6
  —
  15

19) 8
  + 8
  —
  16

20) 7
  + 6
  —
  13

Addition Facts

Add.

1) 5
  + 1
   6

2) 5
  + 3
   8

3) 8
  + 8
   16

4) 4
  + 3
   7

5) 1
  + 3
   4

6) 6
  + 8
   14

7) 5
  + 8
   13

8) 9
  + 3
   12

9) 2
  + 9
   11

10) 1
   + 9
   10

11) 7
   + 2
   9

12) 6
   + 9
   15

13) 9
   + 8
   17

14) 7
   + 6
   13

15) 7
   + 3
   10

16) 9
   + 2
   11

17) 2
   + 4
   6

18) 1
   + 1
   2

19) 3
   + 5
   8

20) 6
   + 1
   7

Addition Facts

Add.

1) 3
  + 7
  ___

2) 3
  + 1
  ___

3) 2
  + 1
  ___

4) 5
  + 8
  ___

5) 8
  + 4
  ___

6) 2
  + 5
  ___

7) 4
  + 7
  ___

8) 2
  + 6
  ___

9) 1
  + 9
  ___

10) 4
  + 2
  ___

11) 3
  + 9
  ___

12) 8
  + 1
  ___

13) 8
  + 3
  ___

14) 8
  + 2
  ___

15) 5
  + 5
  ___

16) 1
  + 7
  ___

17) 6
  + 8
  ___

18) 9
  + 7
  ___

19) 7
  + 5
  ___

20) 3
  + 5
  ___

Addition Facts

Add.

1) 9
   + 1

2) 4
   + 5

3) 3
   + 3

4) 7
   + 1

5) 1
   + 1

6) 3
   + 6

7) 7
   + 7

8) 6
   + 3

9) 8
   + 2

10) 6
    + 7

11) 8
    + 7

12) 8
    + 9

13) 9
    + 2

14) 1
    + 5

15) 1
    + 8

16) 9
    + 6

17) 4
    + 7

18) 4
    + 9

19) 5
    + 9

20) 8
    + 3

www.claymaze.com

Addition Facts

Add.

1)   8
  + 2

2)   9
  + 9

3)   6
  + 7

4)   9
  + 2

5)   2
  + 7

6)   4
  + 6

7)   8
  + 1

8)   5
  + 7

9)   9
  + 6

10)   9
  + 1

11)   2
  + 5

12)   9
  + 4

13)   3
  + 4

14)   2
  + 1

15)   7
  + 4

16)   8
  + 9

17)   6
  + 1

18)   6
  + 3

19)   3
  + 5

20)   2
  + 4

Addition Facts

Add.

1) 6
  + 4

2) 7
  + 4

3) 6
  + 6

4) 5
  + 3

5) 4
  + 1

6) 4
  + 9

7) 8
  + 1

8) 4
  + 6

9) 5
  + 9

10) 2
  + 3

11) 5
  + 2

12) 7
  + 2

13) 7
  + 6

14) 3
  + 2

15) 9
  + 4

16) 2
  + 1

17) 8
  + 8

18) 5
  + 8

19) 7
  + 7

20) 4
  + 2

Addition Facts

Add.

1) 4
  + 5
  ___

2) 1
  + 9
  ___

3) 6
  + 9
  ___

4) 3
  + 4
  ___

5) 5
  + 2
  ___

6) 5
  + 7
  ___

7) 8
  + 3
  ___

8) 3
  + 3
  ___

9) 9
  + 8
  ___

10) 1
  + 7
  ___

11) 9
  + 9
  ___

12) 7
  + 5
  ___

13) 4
  + 8
  ___

14) 5
  + 3
  ___

15) 5
  + 1
  ___

16) 9
  + 1
  ___

17) 5
  + 6
  ___

18) 2
  + 6
  ___

19) 7
  + 2
  ___

20) 2
  + 8
  ___

Addition Facts

Add.

1)   3
 + 8

2)   1
 + 6

3)   7
 + 1

4)   7
 + 6

5)   5
 + 7

6)   4
 + 4

7)   5
 + 8

8)   7
 + 5

9)   7
 + 7

10)   4
 + 2

11)   3
 + 1

12)   3
 + 7

13)   8
 + 3

14)   9
 + 5

15)   6
 + 3

16)   3
 + 9

17)   5
 + 4

18)   7
 + 2

19)   4
 + 9

20)   4
 + 6

www.claymaze.com

Addition Facts

Add.

1)   5
  + 1

2)   3
  + 4

3)   4
  + 9

4)   1
  + 9

5)   4
  + 1

6)   8
  + 2

7)   2
  + 8

8)   1
  + 3

9)   9
  + 2

10)   7
  + 9

11)   5
  + 3

12)   4
  + 2

13)   1
  + 1

14)   8
  + 5

15)   2
  + 9

16)   6
  + 2

17)   3
  + 6

18)   7
  + 6

19)   9
  + 5

20)   6
  + 1

Name _____   Date _____

Addition Facts

Add.

1) 4
   + 5

2) 3
   + 9

3) 4
   + 8

4) 1
   + 6

5) 2
   + 4

6) 5
   + 6

7) 8
   + 5

8) 5
   + 2

9) 2
   + 5

10) 9
    + 5

11) 1
    + 3

12) 3
    + 5

13) 3
    + 2

14) 9
    + 2

15) 3
    + 1

16) 4
    + 2

17) 2
    + 3

18) 7
    + 6

19) 4
    + 9

20) 4
    + 4

SECTION

SUBTRACTION FACTS

11 worksheets
20 problems per sheet

Subtraction Facts

Subtract.

1) $\begin{array}{r} 10 \\ -5 \\ \hline \end{array}$	2) $\begin{array}{r} 6 \\ -3 \\ \hline \end{array}$	3) $\begin{array}{r} 5 \\ -3 \\ \hline \end{array}$	4) $\begin{array}{r} 5 \\ -2 \\ \hline \end{array}$	5) $\begin{array}{r} 2 \\ -2 \\ \hline \end{array}$
6) $\begin{array}{r} 14 \\ -6 \\ \hline \end{array}$	7) $\begin{array}{r} 13 \\ -5 \\ \hline \end{array}$	8) $\begin{array}{r} 6 \\ -4 \\ \hline \end{array}$	9) $\begin{array}{r} 9 \\ -2 \\ \hline \end{array}$	10) $\begin{array}{r} 15 \\ -8 \\ \hline \end{array}$
11) $\begin{array}{r} 18 \\ -9 \\ \hline \end{array}$	12) $\begin{array}{r} 14 \\ -7 \\ \hline \end{array}$	13) $\begin{array}{r} 11 \\ -8 \\ \hline \end{array}$	14) $\begin{array}{r} 5 \\ -5 \\ \hline \end{array}$	15) $\begin{array}{r} 16 \\ -8 \\ \hline \end{array}$
16) $\begin{array}{r} 10 \\ -9 \\ \hline \end{array}$	17) $\begin{array}{r} 3 \\ -1 \\ \hline \end{array}$	18) $\begin{array}{r} 14 \\ -5 \\ \hline \end{array}$	19) $\begin{array}{r} 15 \\ -6 \\ \hline \end{array}$	20) $\begin{array}{r} 4 \\ -3 \\ \hline \end{array}$

Subtraction Facts

Subtract.

1) $\begin{array}{r} 8 \\ -4 \\ \hline \end{array}$
2) $\begin{array}{r} 5 \\ -2 \\ \hline \end{array}$
3) $\begin{array}{r} 14 \\ -6 \\ \hline \end{array}$
4) $\begin{array}{r} 4 \\ -1 \\ \hline \end{array}$
5) $\begin{array}{r} 8 \\ -7 \\ \hline \end{array}$

6) $\begin{array}{r} 15 \\ -8 \\ \hline \end{array}$
7) $\begin{array}{r} 2 \\ -1 \\ \hline \end{array}$
8) $\begin{array}{r} 11 \\ -9 \\ \hline \end{array}$
9) $\begin{array}{r} 16 \\ -9 \\ \hline \end{array}$
10) $\begin{array}{r} 10 \\ -6 \\ \hline \end{array}$

11) $\begin{array}{r} 11 \\ -8 \\ \hline \end{array}$
12) $\begin{array}{r} 18 \\ -9 \\ \hline \end{array}$
13) $\begin{array}{r} 9 \\ -7 \\ \hline \end{array}$
14) $\begin{array}{r} 3 \\ -1 \\ \hline \end{array}$
15) $\begin{array}{r} 5 \\ -1 \\ \hline \end{array}$

16) $\begin{array}{r} 4 \\ -4 \\ \hline \end{array}$
17) $\begin{array}{r} 6 \\ -2 \\ \hline \end{array}$
18) $\begin{array}{r} 12 \\ -4 \\ \hline \end{array}$
19) $\begin{array}{r} 15 \\ -7 \\ \hline \end{array}$
20) $\begin{array}{r} 15 \\ -6 \\ \hline \end{array}$

Name _____   Date _____

Subtraction Facts

Subtract.

1) 17
 - 8
 ___

2) 15
 - 6
 ___

3) 3
 - 3
 ___

4) 3
 - 2
 ___

5) 16
 - 7
 ___

6) 18
 - 9
 ___

7) 13
 - 5
 ___

8) 11
 - 9
 ___

9) 8
 - 3
 ___

10) 8
 - 7
 ___

11) 10
 - 4
 ___

12) 12
 - 8
 ___

13) 3
 - 1
 ___

14) 7
 - 5
 ___

15) 9
 - 6
 ___

16) 16
 - 8
 ___

17) 17
 - 9
 ___

18) 4
 - 3
 ___

19) 11
 - 4
 ___

20) 9
 - 7
 ___

Subtraction Facts

Subtract.

1) $\begin{array}{r} 18 \\ -9 \\ \hline \end{array}$	2) $\begin{array}{r} 2 \\ -1 \\ \hline \end{array}$	3) $\begin{array}{r} 2 \\ -2 \\ \hline \end{array}$	4) $\begin{array}{r} 11 \\ -4 \\ \hline \end{array}$	5) $\begin{array}{r} 6 \\ -1 \\ \hline \end{array}$
6) $\begin{array}{r} 7 \\ -1 \\ \hline \end{array}$	7) $\begin{array}{r} 11 \\ -5 \\ \hline \end{array}$	8) $\begin{array}{r} 10 \\ -5 \\ \hline \end{array}$	9) $\begin{array}{r} 15 \\ -6 \\ \hline \end{array}$	10) $\begin{array}{r} 10 \\ -8 \\ \hline \end{array}$
11) $\begin{array}{r} 11 \\ -7 \\ \hline \end{array}$	12) $\begin{array}{r} 6 \\ -5 \\ \hline \end{array}$	13) $\begin{array}{r} 3 \\ -3 \\ \hline \end{array}$	14) $\begin{array}{r} 15 \\ -7 \\ \hline \end{array}$	15) $\begin{array}{r} 3 \\ -2 \\ \hline \end{array}$
16) $\begin{array}{r} 7 \\ -3 \\ \hline \end{array}$	17) $\begin{array}{r} 10 \\ -1 \\ \hline \end{array}$	18) $\begin{array}{r} 12 \\ -4 \\ \hline \end{array}$	19) $\begin{array}{r} 16 \\ -9 \\ \hline \end{array}$	20) $\begin{array}{r} 17 \\ -9 \\ \hline \end{array}$

Subtraction Facts

Subtract.

1)   2
   -1

2)   15
   -7

3)   12
   -6

4)   12
   -8

5)   9
   -7

6)   3
   -3

7)   6
   -1

8)   10
   -5

9)   11
   -6

10)   16
   -8

11)   7
   -3

12)   7
   -6

13)   8
   -1

14)   9
   -9

15)   11
   -9

16)   6
   -5

17)   14
   -6

18)   8
   -4

19)   10
   -4

20)   14
   -8

Subtraction Facts

Subtract.

1)   4
    − 3

2)   18
   − 9

3)   13
   − 5

4)   3
    − 1

5)   9
    − 2

6)   13
   − 4

7)   12
   − 5

8)   12
   − 6

9)   2
    − 2

10)   8
   − 6

11)   15
   − 9

12)   17
   − 8

13)   13
   − 8

14)   15
   − 7

15)   16
   − 7

16)   14
   − 7

17)   12
   − 4

18)   5
   − 2

19)   4
   − 1

20)   15
   − 6

Subtraction Facts

Subtract.

1)   3
   −3

2)   4
   −2

3)   18
   −9

4)   15
   −9

5)   9
   −8

6)   17
   −8

7)   3
   −2

8)   12
   −4

9)   14
   −7

10)   14
   −5

11)   8
   −6

12)   7
   −4

13)   6
   −5

14)   15
   −7

15)   16
   −7

16)   10
   −5

17)   15
   −8

18)   12
   −9

19)   5
   −4

20)   13
   −9

www.claymaze.com

Subtraction Facts

Subtract.

1)   14
    -9

2)   4
    -2

3)   12
    -3

4)   12
    -8

5)   17
    -9

6)   4
    -1

7)   16
    -9

8)   5
    -4

9)   13
    -9

10)   13
    -6

11)   7
    -5

12)   8
    -1

13)   12
    -7

14)   14
    -8

15)   4
    -3

16)   8
    -2

17)   12
    -5

18)   15
    -9

19)   7
    -2

20)   14
    -6

www.claymaze.com

Subtraction Facts

Subtract.

1) 12
   − 6
   ___

2)   7
   − 7
   ___

3) 11
   − 7
   ___

4)   7
   − 4
   ___

5) 12
   − 8
   ___

6) 18
   − 9
   ___

7) 13
   − 7
   ___

8)   2
   − 2
   ___

9)   7
   − 1
   ___

10) 9
   − 8
   ___

11) 10
   − 6
   ___

12) 10
   − 9
   ___

13) 17
   − 9
   ___

14) 11
   − 2
   ___

15) 11
   − 9
   ___

16) 15
   − 6
   ___

17) 16
   − 8
   ___

18) 8
   − 6
   ___

19) 6
   − 1
   ___

20) 12
   − 9
   ___

Name _____   Date _____

Subtraction Facts

Subtract.

1) $\begin{array}{r} 14 \\ -9 \\ \hline \end{array}$
2) $\begin{array}{r} 16 \\ -7 \\ \hline \end{array}$
3) $\begin{array}{r} 3 \\ -2 \\ \hline \end{array}$
4) $\begin{array}{r} 13 \\ -6 \\ \hline \end{array}$
5) $\begin{array}{r} 5 \\ -4 \\ \hline \end{array}$

6) $\begin{array}{r} 10 \\ -6 \\ \hline \end{array}$
7) $\begin{array}{r} 17 \\ -8 \\ \hline \end{array}$
8) $\begin{array}{r} 18 \\ -9 \\ \hline \end{array}$
9) $\begin{array}{r} 2 \\ -1 \\ \hline \end{array}$
10) $\begin{array}{r} 3 \\ -1 \\ \hline \end{array}$

11) $\begin{array}{r} 4 \\ -1 \\ \hline \end{array}$
12) $\begin{array}{r} 16 \\ -9 \\ \hline \end{array}$
13) $\begin{array}{r} 8 \\ -4 \\ \hline \end{array}$
14) $\begin{array}{r} 2 \\ -2 \\ \hline \end{array}$
15) $\begin{array}{r} 4 \\ -2 \\ \hline \end{array}$

16) $\begin{array}{r} 14 \\ -5 \\ \hline \end{array}$
17) $\begin{array}{r} 8 \\ -7 \\ \hline \end{array}$
18) $\begin{array}{r} 14 \\ -8 \\ \hline \end{array}$
19) $\begin{array}{r} 11 \\ -6 \\ \hline \end{array}$
20) $\begin{array}{r} 6 \\ -2 \\ \hline \end{array}$

www.claymaze.com

Subtraction Facts

Subtract.

1)   15
   −7

2)   7
   −6

3)   16
   −8

4)   15
   −9

5)   12
   −7

6)   13
   −6

7)   5
   −4

8)   16
   −9

9)   9
   −8

10)   10
   −1

11)   10
   −7

12)   3
   −3

13)   9
   −1

14)   9
   −6

15)   6
   −1

16)   6
   −4

17)   15
   −6

18)   15
   −8

19)   4
   −2

20)   8
   −1

2-DIGIT ADDITION
NO REGROUPING

11 worksheets
16 problems per sheet

2 Digit Addition   No Regrouping

Add.

1) $\begin{array}{r} 22 \\ +14 \\ \hline \end{array}$ 2) $\begin{array}{r} 15 \\ +12 \\ \hline \end{array}$ 3) $\begin{array}{r} 18 \\ +11 \\ \hline \end{array}$ 4) $\begin{array}{r} 45 \\ +21 \\ \hline \end{array}$

5) $\begin{array}{r} 34 \\ +10 \\ \hline \end{array}$ 6) $\begin{array}{r} 47 \\ +42 \\ \hline \end{array}$ 7) $\begin{array}{r} 57 \\ +41 \\ \hline \end{array}$ 8) $\begin{array}{r} 31 \\ +27 \\ \hline \end{array}$

9) $\begin{array}{r} 13 \\ +10 \\ \hline \end{array}$ 10) $\begin{array}{r} 52 \\ +36 \\ \hline \end{array}$ 11) $\begin{array}{r} 61 \\ +32 \\ \hline \end{array}$ 12) $\begin{array}{r} 11 \\ +11 \\ \hline \end{array}$

13) $\begin{array}{r} 41 \\ +20 \\ \hline \end{array}$ 14) $\begin{array}{r} 21 \\ +21 \\ \hline \end{array}$ 15) $\begin{array}{r} 12 \\ +11 \\ \hline \end{array}$ 16) $\begin{array}{r} 30 \\ +20 \\ \hline \end{array}$

2 Digit Addition — No Regrouping

Add.

1)
$$\begin{array}{r} 43 \\ +24 \\ \hline \end{array}$$

2)
$$\begin{array}{r} 14 \\ +13 \\ \hline \end{array}$$

3)
$$\begin{array}{r} 60 \\ +22 \\ \hline \end{array}$$

4)
$$\begin{array}{r} 74 \\ +21 \\ \hline \end{array}$$

5)
$$\begin{array}{r} 57 \\ +32 \\ \hline \end{array}$$

6)
$$\begin{array}{r} 24 \\ +14 \\ \hline \end{array}$$

7)
$$\begin{array}{r} 51 \\ +18 \\ \hline \end{array}$$

8)
$$\begin{array}{r} 44 \\ +43 \\ \hline \end{array}$$

9)
$$\begin{array}{r} 27 \\ +21 \\ \hline \end{array}$$

10)
$$\begin{array}{r} 31 \\ +31 \\ \hline \end{array}$$

11)
$$\begin{array}{r} 17 \\ +10 \\ \hline \end{array}$$

12)
$$\begin{array}{r} 41 \\ +36 \\ \hline \end{array}$$

13)
$$\begin{array}{r} 21 \\ +17 \\ \hline \end{array}$$

14)
$$\begin{array}{r} 10 \\ +10 \\ \hline \end{array}$$

15)
$$\begin{array}{r} 12 \\ +12 \\ \hline \end{array}$$

16)
$$\begin{array}{r} 11 \\ +11 \\ \hline \end{array}$$

2 Digit Addition   No Regrouping

Add.

1) 38
  +30

2) 21
  +11

3) 43
  +13

4) 35
  +21

5) 26
  +13

6) 60
  +11

7) 11
  +11

8) 50
  +38

9) 29
  +10

10) 30
  +10

11) 54
  +30

12) 67
  +31

13) 12
  +12

14) 42
  +42

15) 15
  +12

16) 40
  +31

2 Digit Addition | No Regrouping

Add.

1) 24
   +13
   ____

2) 34
   +23
   ____

3) 51
   +16
   ____

4) 25
   +20
   ____

5) 41
   +33
   ____

6) 29
   +10
   ____

7) 84
   +15
   ____

8) 50
   +16
   ____

9) 27
   +21
   ____

10) 26
    +13
    ____

11) 43
    +20
    ____

12) 20
    +11
    ____

13) 15
    +11
    ____

14) 66
    +11
    ____

15) 52
    +35
    ____

16) 47
    +40
    ____

2 Digit Addition — No Regrouping

Add.

1) 47
   +40
   ____

2) 42
   +15
   ____

3) 11
   +10
   ____

4) 71
   +23
   ____

5) 74
   +22
   ____

6) 15
   +13
   ____

7) 36
   +21
   ____

8) 30
   +16
   ____

9) 52
   +36
   ____

10) 75
    +23
    ____

11) 53
    +12
    ____

12) 61
    +37
    ____

13) 10
    +10
    ____

14) 62
    +26
    ____

15) 63
    +24
    ____

16) 45
    +31
    ____

2 Digit Addition No Regrouping

Add.

1)
```
  45
+ 42
----
```

2)
```
  31
+ 25
----
```

3)
```
  74
+ 14
----
```

4)
```
  21
+ 13
----
```

5)
```
  36
+ 30
----
```

6)
```
  24
+ 24
----
```

7)
```
  30
+ 29
----
```

8)
```
  35
+ 33
----
```

9)
```
  32
+ 14
----
```

10)
```
  43
+ 23
----
```

11)
```
  51
+ 34
----
```

12)
```
  11
+ 11
----
```

13)
```
  40
+ 40
----
```

14)
```
  44
+ 40
----
```

15)
```
  41
+ 21
----
```

16)
```
  52
+ 31
----
```

2 Digit Addition | No Regrouping

Add.

1) $\begin{array}{r} 45 \\ +43 \\ \hline \end{array}$
2) $\begin{array}{r} 52 \\ +47 \\ \hline \end{array}$
3) $\begin{array}{r} 65 \\ +30 \\ \hline \end{array}$
4) $\begin{array}{r} 31 \\ +17 \\ \hline \end{array}$

5) $\begin{array}{r} 71 \\ +13 \\ \hline \end{array}$
6) $\begin{array}{r} 58 \\ +20 \\ \hline \end{array}$
7) $\begin{array}{r} 60 \\ +16 \\ \hline \end{array}$
8) $\begin{array}{r} 19 \\ +10 \\ \hline \end{array}$

9) $\begin{array}{r} 42 \\ +23 \\ \hline \end{array}$
10) $\begin{array}{r} 24 \\ +14 \\ \hline \end{array}$
11) $\begin{array}{r} 22 \\ +12 \\ \hline \end{array}$
12) $\begin{array}{r} 30 \\ +24 \\ \hline \end{array}$

13) $\begin{array}{r} 40 \\ +30 \\ \hline \end{array}$
14) $\begin{array}{r} 44 \\ +10 \\ \hline \end{array}$
15) $\begin{array}{r} 66 \\ +32 \\ \hline \end{array}$
16) $\begin{array}{r} 73 \\ +26 \\ \hline \end{array}$

2 Digit Addition   No Regrouping

Add.

1)
```
  5 0
+ 3 0
-----
```

2)
```
  7 1
+ 2 5
-----
```

3)
```
  3 5
+ 1 1
-----
```

4)
```
  1 1
+ 1 1
-----
```

5)
```
  7 0
+ 1 0
-----
```

6)
```
  2 0
+ 1 5
-----
```

7)
```
  5 8
+ 1 1
-----
```

8)
```
  5 3
+ 2 3
-----
```

9)
```
  4 5
+ 2 4
-----
```

10)
```
  6 9
+ 2 0
-----
```

11)
```
  3 0
+ 1 8
-----
```

12)
```
  6 3
+ 3 5
-----
```

13)
```
  3 3
+ 2 5
-----
```

14)
```
  3 4
+ 3 1
-----
```

15)
```
  1 3
+ 1 3
-----
```

16)
```
  2 1
+ 1 2
-----
```

2 Digit Addition No Regrouping

Add.

1) $\begin{array}{r} 72 \\ +10 \\ \hline \end{array}$
2) $\begin{array}{r} 46 \\ +42 \\ \hline \end{array}$
3) $\begin{array}{r} 20 \\ +10 \\ \hline \end{array}$
4) $\begin{array}{r} 57 \\ +42 \\ \hline \end{array}$

5) $\begin{array}{r} 33 \\ +22 \\ \hline \end{array}$
6) $\begin{array}{r} 37 \\ +20 \\ \hline \end{array}$
7) $\begin{array}{r} 26 \\ +11 \\ \hline \end{array}$
8) $\begin{array}{r} 13 \\ +11 \\ \hline \end{array}$

9) $\begin{array}{r} 34 \\ +20 \\ \hline \end{array}$
10) $\begin{array}{r} 78 \\ +10 \\ \hline \end{array}$
11) $\begin{array}{r} 51 \\ +10 \\ \hline \end{array}$
12) $\begin{array}{r} 10 \\ +10 \\ \hline \end{array}$

13) $\begin{array}{r} 14 \\ +12 \\ \hline \end{array}$
14) $\begin{array}{r} 50 \\ +10 \\ \hline \end{array}$
15) $\begin{array}{r} 16 \\ +13 \\ \hline \end{array}$
16) $\begin{array}{r} 29 \\ +10 \\ \hline \end{array}$

2 Digit Addition No Regrouping

Add.

1) 52
   +44
   ‾‾‾‾

2) 50
   +36
   ‾‾‾‾

3) 47
   +22
   ‾‾‾‾

4) 63
   +35
   ‾‾‾‾

5) 73
   +10
   ‾‾‾‾

6) 71
   +22
   ‾‾‾‾

7) 20
   +17
   ‾‾‾‾

8) 31
   +11
   ‾‾‾‾

9) 12
   +11
   ‾‾‾‾

10) 44
    +20
    ‾‾‾‾

11) 43
    +22
    ‾‾‾‾

12) 22
    +15
    ‾‾‾‾

13) 76
    +12
    ‾‾‾‾

14) 18
    +10
    ‾‾‾‾

15) 60
    +29
    ‾‾‾‾

16) 24
    +10
    ‾‾‾‾

2 Digit Addition No Regrouping

Add.

1) $\begin{array}{r} 30 \\ +12 \\ \hline \end{array}$
2) $\begin{array}{r} 62 \\ +36 \\ \hline \end{array}$
3) $\begin{array}{r} 32 \\ +32 \\ \hline \end{array}$
4) $\begin{array}{r} 25 \\ +12 \\ \hline \end{array}$

5) $\begin{array}{r} 31 \\ +17 \\ \hline \end{array}$
6) $\begin{array}{r} 17 \\ +11 \\ \hline \end{array}$
7) $\begin{array}{r} 66 \\ +13 \\ \hline \end{array}$
8) $\begin{array}{r} 15 \\ +14 \\ \hline \end{array}$

9) $\begin{array}{r} 44 \\ +20 \\ \hline \end{array}$
10) $\begin{array}{r} 22 \\ +15 \\ \hline \end{array}$
11) $\begin{array}{r} 46 \\ +33 \\ \hline \end{array}$
12) $\begin{array}{r} 48 \\ +20 \\ \hline \end{array}$

13) $\begin{array}{r} 16 \\ +11 \\ \hline \end{array}$
14) $\begin{array}{r} 57 \\ +30 \\ \hline \end{array}$
15) $\begin{array}{r} 40 \\ +22 \\ \hline \end{array}$
16) $\begin{array}{r} 23 \\ +14 \\ \hline \end{array}$

SECTION

2-DIGIT
ADDITION
WITH REGROUPING

11 worksheets
16 problems per sheet

2 Digit Addition | With Regrouping

Add.

1)
$$
\begin{array}{r}
28 \\
+13 \\
\hline
\end{array}
$$

2)
$$
\begin{array}{r}
58 \\
+26 \\
\hline
\end{array}
$$

3)
$$
\begin{array}{r}
99 \\
+98 \\
\hline
\end{array}
$$

4)
$$
\begin{array}{r}
93 \\
+78 \\
\hline
\end{array}
$$

5)
$$
\begin{array}{r}
29 \\
+14 \\
\hline
\end{array}
$$

6)
$$
\begin{array}{r}
45 \\
+29 \\
\hline
\end{array}
$$

7)
$$
\begin{array}{r}
17 \\
+15 \\
\hline
\end{array}
$$

8)
$$
\begin{array}{r}
19 \\
+18 \\
\hline
\end{array}
$$

9)
$$
\begin{array}{r}
26 \\
+26 \\
\hline
\end{array}
$$

10)
$$
\begin{array}{r}
34 \\
+29 \\
\hline
\end{array}
$$

11)
$$
\begin{array}{r}
55 \\
+19 \\
\hline
\end{array}
$$

12)
$$
\begin{array}{r}
75 \\
+38 \\
\hline
\end{array}
$$

13)
$$
\begin{array}{r}
27 \\
+18 \\
\hline
\end{array}
$$

14)
$$
\begin{array}{r}
86 \\
+77 \\
\hline
\end{array}
$$

15)
$$
\begin{array}{r}
84 \\
+27 \\
\hline
\end{array}
$$

16)
$$
\begin{array}{r}
68 \\
+45 \\
\hline
\end{array}
$$

2 Digit Addition With Regrouping

Add.

1) 69
  + 25
  ‾‾‾‾

2) 77
  + 35
  ‾‾‾‾

3) 59
  + 45
  ‾‾‾‾

4) 78
  + 26
  ‾‾‾‾

5) 88
  + 85
  ‾‾‾‾

6) 58
  + 33
  ‾‾‾‾

7) 27
  + 24
  ‾‾‾‾

8) 48
  + 44
  ‾‾‾‾

9) 19
  + 19
  ‾‾‾‾

10) 49
   + 22
   ‾‾‾‾

11) 39
   + 32
   ‾‾‾‾

12) 57
   + 28
   ‾‾‾‾

13) 37
   + 28
   ‾‾‾‾

14) 38
   + 33
   ‾‾‾‾

15) 29
   + 27
   ‾‾‾‾

16) 56
   + 39
   ‾‾‾‾

www.claymaze.com

2 Digit Addition With Regrouping

Add.

1) $\begin{array}{r} 16 \\ +15 \\ \hline \end{array}$	2) $\begin{array}{r} 94 \\ +49 \\ \hline \end{array}$	3) $\begin{array}{r} 46 \\ +35 \\ \hline \end{array}$	4) $\begin{array}{r} 58 \\ +18 \\ \hline \end{array}$
5) $\begin{array}{r} 29 \\ +17 \\ \hline \end{array}$	6) $\begin{array}{r} 47 \\ +19 \\ \hline \end{array}$	7) $\begin{array}{r} 38 \\ +15 \\ \hline \end{array}$	8) $\begin{array}{r} 43 \\ +28 \\ \hline \end{array}$
9) $\begin{array}{r} 79 \\ +45 \\ \hline \end{array}$	10) $\begin{array}{r} 88 \\ +66 \\ \hline \end{array}$	11) $\begin{array}{r} 28 \\ +28 \\ \hline \end{array}$	12) $\begin{array}{r} 57 \\ +45 \\ \hline \end{array}$
13) $\begin{array}{r} 19 \\ +15 \\ \hline \end{array}$	14) $\begin{array}{r} 65 \\ +46 \\ \hline \end{array}$	15) $\begin{array}{r} 97 \\ +27 \\ \hline \end{array}$	16) $\begin{array}{r} 82 \\ +69 \\ \hline \end{array}$

2 Digit Addition   With Regrouping

Add.

1)   48
    +19
    ————

2)   29
    +24
    ————

3)   98
    +35
    ————

4)   46
    +17
    ————

5)   44
    +17
    ————

6)   39
    +13
    ————

7)   76
    +36
    ————

8)   95
    +38
    ————

9)   54
    +39
    ————

10)   59
    +27
    ————

11)   97
    +65
    ————

12)   16
    +16
    ————

13)   67
    +45
    ————

14)   19
    +12
    ————

15)   69
    +59
    ————

16)   58
    +18
    ————

2 Digit Addition   With Regrouping

Add.

1)   99
   +18
___

2)   67
   +44
___

3)   77
   +77
___

4)   96
   +68
___

5)   86
   +59
___

6)   49
   +45
___

7)   97
   +68
___

8)   94
   +77
___

9)   79
   +69
___

10)   59
   +26
___

11)   95
   +56
___

12)   54
   +17
___

13)   29
   +19
___

14)   89
   +53
___

15)   74
   +29
___

16)   19
   +12
___

2 Digit Addition With Regrouping

Add.

1) 29
   +13
   ____

2) 19
   +16
   ____

3) 58
   +19
   ____

4) 98
   +54
   ____

5) 77
   +35
   ____

6) 48
   +29
   ____

7) 76
   +37
   ____

8) 99
   +78
   ____

9) 47
   +16
   ____

10) 52
    +49
    ____

11) 79
    +47
    ____

12) 32
    +29
    ____

13) 38
    +25
    ____

14) 16
    +15
    ____

15) 55
    +29
    ____

16) 75
    +69
    ____

2 Digit Addition | With Regrouping

Add.

1) 85
   +56
   ____

2) 18
   +14
   ____

3) 23
   +19
   ____

4) 28
   +24
   ____

5) 96
   +19
   ____

6) 19
   +17
   ____

7) 97
   +64
   ____

8) 56
   +16
   ____

9) 89
   +54
   ____

10) 68
   +46
   ____

11) 72
   +49
   ____

12) 37
   +25
   ____

13) 77
   +28
   ____

14) 84
   +77
   ____

15) 98
   +25
   ____

16) 24
   +18
   ____

2 Digit Addition | With Regrouping

Add.

1)   95
    +48
    ─────

2)   18
    +17
    ─────

3)   99
    +29
    ─────

4)   65
    +39
    ─────

5)   83
    +78
    ─────

6)   17
    +14
    ─────

7)   82
    +39
    ─────

8)   67
    +37
    ─────

9)   66
    +38
    ─────

10) 49
    +27
    ─────

11) 79
    +22
    ─────

12) 48
    +36
    ─────

13) 46
    +18
    ─────

14) 29
    +24
    ─────

15) 28
    +27
    ─────

16) 19
    +14
    ─────

2 Digit Addition With Regrouping

Add.

1)   84
   +69

2)   37
   +15

3)   88
   +88

4)   97
   +25

5)   39
   +19

6)   96
   +18

7)   33
   +18

8)   86
   +65

9)   17
   +14

10)   76
   +38

11)   98
   +35

12)   49
   +34

13)   68
   +35

14)   94
   +17

15)   56
   +56

16)   42
   +39

2 Digit Addition With Regrouping

Add.

1) $\begin{array}{r} 78 \\ +38 \\ \hline \end{array}$

2) $\begin{array}{r} 99 \\ +43 \\ \hline \end{array}$

3) $\begin{array}{r} 26 \\ +25 \\ \hline \end{array}$

4) $\begin{array}{r} 56 \\ +29 \\ \hline \end{array}$

5) $\begin{array}{r} 38 \\ +18 \\ \hline \end{array}$

6) $\begin{array}{r} 44 \\ +19 \\ \hline \end{array}$

7) $\begin{array}{r} 68 \\ +58 \\ \hline \end{array}$

8) $\begin{array}{r} 58 \\ +56 \\ \hline \end{array}$

9) $\begin{array}{r} 57 \\ +35 \\ \hline \end{array}$

10) $\begin{array}{r} 37 \\ +35 \\ \hline \end{array}$

11) $\begin{array}{r} 46 \\ +29 \\ \hline \end{array}$

12) $\begin{array}{r} 89 \\ +25 \\ \hline \end{array}$

13) $\begin{array}{r} 97 \\ +39 \\ \hline \end{array}$

14) $\begin{array}{r} 62 \\ +59 \\ \hline \end{array}$

15) $\begin{array}{r} 75 \\ +36 \\ \hline \end{array}$

16) $\begin{array}{r} 63 \\ +29 \\ \hline \end{array}$

www.claymaze.com

2 Digit Addition With Regrouping

Add.

1)   3 7
  + 3 5
    2

2)   3 3
  + 2 9
    2

3)   4 7
  + 3 7
    8 4

4)   8 9
  + 8 2
   1 7 1

5)   8 5
  + 5 6
   1 4 1

6)   5 9
  + 3 7
    9 6

7)   9 4
  + 8 7
   1 8 1

8)   5 4
  + 3 7
    9 1

9)   4 4
  + 1 7
    6 1

10)   4 5
  + 2 6
    7 1

11)   2 7
  + 1 8
    4 5

12)   1 8
  + 1 4
    3 2

13)   4 3
  + 2 8
    7 1

14)   3 9
  + 1 7
    5 6

15)   4 9
  + 1 2
    6 1

16)   2 8
  + 1 4
    4 2

SECTION

2-DIGIT SUBTRACTION
NO REGROUPING

11 worksheets
16 problems per sheet

2 Digit Subtraction No Regrouping

Subtract.

1) 69
   -37
   ____

2) 99
   -45
   ____

3) 89
   -75
   ____

4) 32
   -10
   ____

5) 29
   -11
   ____

6) 49
   -36
   ____

7) 46
   -15
   ____

8) 34
   -33
   ____

9) 24
   -10
   ____

10) 88
    -31
    ____

11) 56
    -33
    ____

12) 16
    -14
    ____

13) 78
    -56
    ____

14) 54
    -21
    ____

15) 52
    -50
    ____

16) 12
    -11
    ____

www.claymaze.com

2 Digit Subtraction No Regrouping

Subtract.

1) $\begin{array}{r} 77 \\ -51 \\ \hline \end{array}$
2) $\begin{array}{r} 79 \\ -41 \\ \hline \end{array}$
3) $\begin{array}{r} 16 \\ -14 \\ \hline \end{array}$
4) $\begin{array}{r} 27 \\ -20 \\ \hline \end{array}$

5) $\begin{array}{r} 24 \\ -11 \\ \hline \end{array}$
6) $\begin{array}{r} 49 \\ -34 \\ \hline \end{array}$
7) $\begin{array}{r} 19 \\ -12 \\ \hline \end{array}$
8) $\begin{array}{r} 11 \\ -10 \\ \hline \end{array}$

9) $\begin{array}{r} 67 \\ -32 \\ \hline \end{array}$
10) $\begin{array}{r} 39 \\ -33 \\ \hline \end{array}$
11) $\begin{array}{r} 59 \\ -45 \\ \hline \end{array}$
12) $\begin{array}{r} 69 \\ -65 \\ \hline \end{array}$

13) $\begin{array}{r} 98 \\ -75 \\ \hline \end{array}$
14) $\begin{array}{r} 76 \\ -42 \\ \hline \end{array}$
15) $\begin{array}{r} 68 \\ -33 \\ \hline \end{array}$
16) $\begin{array}{r} 48 \\ -26 \\ \hline \end{array}$

2 Digit Subtraction No Regrouping

Subtract.

1) 77
   -24
   ____

2) 43
   -31
   ____

3) 26
   -15
   ____

4) 81
   -60
   ____

5) 47
   -31
   ____

6) 52
   -11
   ____

7) 79
   -27
   ____

8) 36
   -12
   ____

9) 75
   -13
   ____

10) 92
   -31
   ____

11) 88
   -43
   ____

12) 84
   -42
   ____

13) 99
   -17
   ____

14) 11
   -10
   ____

15) 97
   -30
   ____

16) 72
   -31
   ____

2 Digit Subtraction No Regrouping

Subtract.

1) $\begin{array}{r} 78 \\ -23 \\ \hline \end{array}$
2) $\begin{array}{r} 95 \\ -81 \\ \hline \end{array}$
3) $\begin{array}{r} 67 \\ -40 \\ \hline \end{array}$
4) $\begin{array}{r} 27 \\ -23 \\ \hline \end{array}$

5) $\begin{array}{r} 35 \\ -20 \\ \hline \end{array}$
6) $\begin{array}{r} 87 \\ -70 \\ \hline \end{array}$
7) $\begin{array}{r} 79 \\ -40 \\ \hline \end{array}$
8) $\begin{array}{r} 69 \\ -56 \\ \hline \end{array}$

9) $\begin{array}{r} 99 \\ -60 \\ \hline \end{array}$
10) $\begin{array}{r} 92 \\ -10 \\ \hline \end{array}$
11) $\begin{array}{r} 34 \\ -11 \\ \hline \end{array}$
12) $\begin{array}{r} 12 \\ -11 \\ \hline \end{array}$

13) $\begin{array}{r} 84 \\ -43 \\ \hline \end{array}$
14) $\begin{array}{r} 29 \\ -21 \\ \hline \end{array}$
15) $\begin{array}{r} 39 \\ -23 \\ \hline \end{array}$
16) $\begin{array}{r} 48 \\ -43 \\ \hline \end{array}$

2 Digit Subtraction   No Regrouping

Subtract.

1)   64
    − 53

2)   96
    − 81

3)   45
    − 11

4)   66
    − 65

5)   48
    − 34

6)   27
    − 25

7)   28
    − 11

8)   69
    − 34

9)   79
    − 61

10)   19
    − 16

11)   99
    − 64

12)   24
    − 20

13)   89
    − 11

14)   16
    − 15

15)   37
    − 20

16)   35
    − 10

www.claymaze.com

2 Digit Subtraction No Regrouping

Subtract.

1)
```
  9 9
- 7 1
```

2)
```
  8 9
- 5 0
```

3)
```
  5 6
- 5 2
```

4)
```
  4 1
- 1 0
```

5)
```
  2 4
- 2 2
```

6)
```
  1 8
- 1 5
```

7)
```
  7 7
- 3 0
```

8)
```
  8 3
- 5 2
```

9)
```
  4 6
- 2 4
```

10)
```
  5 9
- 1 7
```

11)
```
  9 7
- 8 1
```

12)
```
  1 7
- 1 5
```

13)
```
  9 6
- 5 3
```

14)
```
  3 7
- 3 4
```

15)
```
  1 6
- 1 4
```

16)
```
  8 7
- 6 1
```

2 Digit Subtraction   No Regrouping

Subtract.

1) 38
   -17

2) 54
   -30

3) 86
   -13

4) 14
   -13

5) 15
   -11

6) 27
   -22

7) 34
   -10

8) 99
   -35

9) 48
   -25

10) 47
   -42

11) 57
   -41

12) 95
   -70

13) 89
   -68

14) 13
   -10

15) 28
   -17

16) 49
   -23

Name _____   Date _____

2 Digit Subtraction   No Regrouping

Subtract.

1) $\begin{array}{r} 28 \\ -10 \\ \hline \end{array}$

2) $\begin{array}{r} 15 \\ -13 \\ \hline \end{array}$

3) $\begin{array}{r} 65 \\ -30 \\ \hline \end{array}$

4) $\begin{array}{r} 58 \\ -44 \\ \hline \end{array}$

5) $\begin{array}{r} 78 \\ -70 \\ \hline \end{array}$

6) $\begin{array}{r} 18 \\ -12 \\ \hline \end{array}$

7) $\begin{array}{r} 38 \\ -37 \\ \hline \end{array}$

8) $\begin{array}{r} 48 \\ -27 \\ \hline \end{array}$

9) $\begin{array}{r} 83 \\ -30 \\ \hline \end{array}$

10) $\begin{array}{r} 23 \\ -12 \\ \hline \end{array}$

11) $\begin{array}{r} 73 \\ -70 \\ \hline \end{array}$

12) $\begin{array}{r} 89 \\ -22 \\ \hline \end{array}$

13) $\begin{array}{r} 53 \\ -22 \\ \hline \end{array}$

14) $\begin{array}{r} 98 \\ -53 \\ \hline \end{array}$

15) $\begin{array}{r} 17 \\ -14 \\ \hline \end{array}$

16) $\begin{array}{r} 47 \\ -32 \\ \hline \end{array}$

2 Digit Subtraction | No Regrouping

Subtract.

1)   43
   −11
   ‾‾‾‾

2)   67
   −20
   ‾‾‾‾

3)   12
   −10
   ‾‾‾‾

4)   28
   −14
   ‾‾‾‾

5)   96
   −44
   ‾‾‾‾

6)   92
   −31
   ‾‾‾‾

7)   65
   −22
   ‾‾‾‾

8)   68
   −44
   ‾‾‾‾

9)   93
   −80
   ‾‾‾‾

10)   87
   −35
   ‾‾‾‾

11)   75
   −50
   ‾‾‾‾

12)   39
   −35
   ‾‾‾‾

13)   89
   −12
   ‾‾‾‾

14)   19
   −15
   ‾‾‾‾

15)   38
   −25
   ‾‾‾‾

16)   86
   −64
   ‾‾‾‾

2 Digit Subtraction No Regrouping

Subtract.

1) $\begin{array}{r} 66 \\ -21 \\ \hline \end{array}$

2) $\begin{array}{r} 39 \\ -18 \\ \hline \end{array}$

3) $\begin{array}{r} 92 \\ -50 \\ \hline \end{array}$

4) $\begin{array}{r} 37 \\ -21 \\ \hline \end{array}$

5) $\begin{array}{r} 35 \\ -34 \\ \hline \end{array}$

6) $\begin{array}{r} 69 \\ -63 \\ \hline \end{array}$

7) $\begin{array}{r} 59 \\ -28 \\ \hline \end{array}$

8) $\begin{array}{r} 57 \\ -56 \\ \hline \end{array}$

9) $\begin{array}{r} 38 \\ -10 \\ \hline \end{array}$

10) $\begin{array}{r} 17 \\ -14 \\ \hline \end{array}$

11) $\begin{array}{r} 58 \\ -34 \\ \hline \end{array}$

12) $\begin{array}{r} 94 \\ -51 \\ \hline \end{array}$

13) $\begin{array}{r} 43 \\ -11 \\ \hline \end{array}$

14) $\begin{array}{r} 76 \\ -45 \\ \hline \end{array}$

15) $\begin{array}{r} 85 \\ -42 \\ \hline \end{array}$

16) $\begin{array}{r} 32 \\ -20 \\ \hline \end{array}$

2 Digit Subtraction   No Regrouping

Subtract.

1)   73
   − 41

2)   67
   − 54

3)   25
   − 13

4)   17
   − 14

5)   68
   − 14

6)   66
   − 11

7)   33
   − 10

8)   75
   − 51

9)   37
   − 32

10)   89
   − 70

11)   15
   − 14

12)   12
   − 11

13)   88
   − 23

14)   24
   − 10

15)   27
   − 21

16)   96
   − 22

SECTION

2-DIGIT SUBTRACTION
WITH REGROUPING

11 worksheets
16 problems per sheet

2 Digit Subtraction With Regrouping

Subtract.

1)   34
    − 27
    ‾‾‾‾

2)   80
    − 23
    ‾‾‾‾

3)   67
    − 48
    ‾‾‾‾

4)   90
    − 89
    ‾‾‾‾

5)   72
    − 34
    ‾‾‾‾

6)   33
    − 25
    ‾‾‾‾

7)   20
    − 19
    ‾‾‾‾

8)   65
    − 39
    ‾‾‾‾

9)   52
    − 19
    ‾‾‾‾

10)   87
     − 38
     ‾‾‾‾

11)   41
     − 19
     ‾‾‾‾

12)   54
     − 15
     ‾‾‾‾

13)   82
     − 75
     ‾‾‾‾

14)   60
     − 48
     ‾‾‾‾

15)   23
     − 17
     ‾‾‾‾

16)   30
     − 18
     ‾‾‾‾

www.claymaze.com

2 Digit Subtraction | With Regrouping

Subtract.

1) $\begin{array}{r} 61 \\ -49 \\ \hline \end{array}$

2) $\begin{array}{r} 60 \\ -22 \\ \hline \end{array}$

3) $\begin{array}{r} 47 \\ -18 \\ \hline \end{array}$

4) $\begin{array}{r} 83 \\ -27 \\ \hline \end{array}$

5) $\begin{array}{r} 63 \\ -15 \\ \hline \end{array}$

6) $\begin{array}{r} 31 \\ -18 \\ \hline \end{array}$

7) $\begin{array}{r} 92 \\ -56 \\ \hline \end{array}$

8) $\begin{array}{r} 97 \\ -89 \\ \hline \end{array}$

9) $\begin{array}{r} 71 \\ -39 \\ \hline \end{array}$

10) $\begin{array}{r} 41 \\ -29 \\ \hline \end{array}$

11) $\begin{array}{r} 81 \\ -16 \\ \hline \end{array}$

12) $\begin{array}{r} 91 \\ -23 \\ \hline \end{array}$

13) $\begin{array}{r} 66 \\ -49 \\ \hline \end{array}$

14) $\begin{array}{r} 52 \\ -27 \\ \hline \end{array}$

15) $\begin{array}{r} 94 \\ -27 \\ \hline \end{array}$

16) $\begin{array}{r} 30 \\ -11 \\ \hline \end{array}$

www.claymaze.com

2 Digit Subtraction With Regrouping

Subtract.

1) 78
   -59

2) 25
   -19

3) 91
   -62

4) 75
   -58

5) 31
   -12

6) 44
   -29

7) 71
   -14

8) 23
   -17

9) 51
   -48

10) 90
    -34

11) 92
    -29

12) 60
    -45

13) 34
    -19

14) 81
    -68

15) 73
    -45

16) 70
    -55

2 Digit Subtraction With Regrouping

Subtract.

1)   83
   − 1 5
   ———

2)   63
   − 3 8
   ———

3)   40
   − 1 3
   ———

4)   50
   − 2 3
   ———

5)   71
   − 6 5
   ———

6)   60
   − 2 7
   ———

7)   22
   − 1 7
   ———

8)   72
   − 6 7
   ———

9)   70
   − 5 3
   ———

10)   41
    − 1 6
    ———

11)   92
    − 8 5
    ———

12)   74
    − 1 5
    ———

13)   75
    − 3 6
    ———

14)   61
    − 2 5
    ———

15)   43
    − 3 5
    ———

16)   64
    − 1 9
    ———

2 Digit Subtraction With Regrouping

Subtract.

1) 64 −18	2) 31 −23	3) 50 −19	4) 81 −16
5) 53 −34	6) 84 −48	7) 51 −16	8) 23 −17
9) 90 −52	10) 33 −15	11) 56 −19	12) 43 −15
13) 41 −39	14) 46 −29	15) 83 −24	16) 55 −46

www.claymaze.com

2 Digit Subtraction With Regrouping

Subtract.

1) $\begin{array}{r} 50 \\ -45 \\ \hline \end{array}$

2) $\begin{array}{r} 52 \\ -17 \\ \hline \end{array}$

3) $\begin{array}{r} 41 \\ -27 \\ \hline \end{array}$

4) $\begin{array}{r} 71 \\ -18 \\ \hline \end{array}$

5) $\begin{array}{r} 80 \\ -22 \\ \hline \end{array}$

6) $\begin{array}{r} 62 \\ -13 \\ \hline \end{array}$

7) $\begin{array}{r} 53 \\ -14 \\ \hline \end{array}$

8) $\begin{array}{r} 63 \\ -27 \\ \hline \end{array}$

9) $\begin{array}{r} 30 \\ -11 \\ \hline \end{array}$

10) $\begin{array}{r} 33 \\ -25 \\ \hline \end{array}$

11) $\begin{array}{r} 83 \\ -17 \\ \hline \end{array}$

12) $\begin{array}{r} 90 \\ -26 \\ \hline \end{array}$

13) $\begin{array}{r} 60 \\ -11 \\ \hline \end{array}$

14) $\begin{array}{r} 31 \\ -15 \\ \hline \end{array}$

15) $\begin{array}{r} 23 \\ -18 \\ \hline \end{array}$

16) $\begin{array}{r} 96 \\ -17 \\ \hline \end{array}$

www.claymaze.com

2 Digit Subtraction | With Regrouping

Subtract.

1) $\begin{array}{r} 87 \\ -48 \\ \hline \end{array}$ 2) $\begin{array}{r} 31 \\ -26 \\ \hline \end{array}$ 3) $\begin{array}{r} 96 \\ -67 \\ \hline \end{array}$ 4) $\begin{array}{r} 63 \\ -24 \\ \hline \end{array}$

5) $\begin{array}{r} 74 \\ -26 \\ \hline \end{array}$ 6) $\begin{array}{r} 80 \\ -36 \\ \hline \end{array}$ 7) $\begin{array}{r} 21 \\ -15 \\ \hline \end{array}$ 8) $\begin{array}{r} 24 \\ -18 \\ \hline \end{array}$

9) $\begin{array}{r} 28 \\ -19 \\ \hline \end{array}$ 10) $\begin{array}{r} 70 \\ -44 \\ \hline \end{array}$ 11) $\begin{array}{r} 82 \\ -67 \\ \hline \end{array}$ 12) $\begin{array}{r} 34 \\ -27 \\ \hline \end{array}$

13) $\begin{array}{r} 90 \\ -89 \\ \hline \end{array}$ 14) $\begin{array}{r} 72 \\ -34 \\ \hline \end{array}$ 15) $\begin{array}{r} 62 \\ -27 \\ \hline \end{array}$ 16) $\begin{array}{r} 84 \\ -29 \\ \hline \end{array}$

2 Digit Subtraction   With Regrouping

Subtract.

1)
```
  52
- 36
----
```

2)
```
  81
- 63
----
```

3)
```
  46
- 27
----
```

4)
```
  76
- 58
----
```

5)
```
  55
- 16
----
```

6)
```
  72
- 27
----
```

7)
```
  96
- 57
----
```

8)
```
  24
- 17
----
```

9)
```
  47
- 19
----
```

10)
```
  23
- 14
----
```

11)
```
  51
- 29
----
```

12)
```
  41
- 39
----
```

13)
```
  36
- 18
----
```

14)
```
  75
- 59
----
```

15)
```
  80
- 42
----
```

16)
```
  42
- 24
----
```

2 Digit Subtraction | With Regrouping

Subtract.

1) 72
   -48
   ____

2) 82
   -43
   ____

3) 60
   -52
   ____

4) 65
   -18
   ____

5) 43
   -18
   ____

6) 40
   -28
   ____

7) 83
   -17
   ____

8) 33
   -25
   ____

9) 31
   -14
   ____

10) 93
   -18
   ____

11) 90
   -14
   ____

12) 36
   -28
   ____

13) 21
   -16
   ____

14) 62
   -46
   ____

15) 30
   -29
   ____

16) 45
   -36
   ____

2 Digit Subtraction With Regrouping

Subtract.

1) 93
  − 35

2) 90
  − 76

3) 43
  − 37

4) 75
  − 29

5) 44
  − 38

6) 62
  − 59

7) 74
  − 15

8) 41
  − 19

9) 45
  − 37

10) 42
  − 37

11) 30
  − 19

12) 22
  − 19

13) 20
  − 16

14) 95
  − 49

15) 87
  − 48

16) 61
  − 28

2 Digit Subtraction | With Regrouping

Subtract.

1) $\begin{array}{r} 80 \\ -64 \\ \hline \end{array}$ 2) $\begin{array}{r} 50 \\ -14 \\ \hline \end{array}$ 3) $\begin{array}{r} 22 \\ -14 \\ \hline \end{array}$ 4) $\begin{array}{r} 61 \\ -26 \\ \hline \end{array}$

5) $\begin{array}{r} 40 \\ -29 \\ \hline \end{array}$ 6) $\begin{array}{r} 70 \\ -38 \\ \hline \end{array}$ 7) $\begin{array}{r} 91 \\ -32 \\ \hline \end{array}$ 8) $\begin{array}{r} 54 \\ -29 \\ \hline \end{array}$

9) $\begin{array}{r} 42 \\ -25 \\ \hline \end{array}$ 10) $\begin{array}{r} 51 \\ -43 \\ \hline \end{array}$ 11) $\begin{array}{r} 62 \\ -16 \\ \hline \end{array}$ 12) $\begin{array}{r} 34 \\ -17 \\ \hline \end{array}$

13) $\begin{array}{r} 95 \\ -26 \\ \hline \end{array}$ 14) $\begin{array}{r} 30 \\ -14 \\ \hline \end{array}$ 15) $\begin{array}{r} 96 \\ -78 \\ \hline \end{array}$ 16) $\begin{array}{r} 71 \\ -63 \\ \hline \end{array}$

SECTION

3-DIGIT
ADDITION
NO REGROUPING

11 worksheets
16 problems per sheet

3 Digit Addition   No Regrouping

Add.

1) $\begin{array}{r} 222 \\ +153 \\ \hline \end{array}$ 2) $\begin{array}{r} 643 \\ +326 \\ \hline \end{array}$ 3) $\begin{array}{r} 361 \\ +510 \\ \hline \end{array}$ 4) $\begin{array}{r} 214 \\ +464 \\ \hline \end{array}$

5) $\begin{array}{r} 462 \\ +100 \\ \hline \end{array}$ 6) $\begin{array}{r} 524 \\ +303 \\ \hline \end{array}$ 7) $\begin{array}{r} 572 \\ +217 \\ \hline \end{array}$ 8) $\begin{array}{r} 745 \\ +234 \\ \hline \end{array}$

9) $\begin{array}{r} 423 \\ +156 \\ \hline \end{array}$ 10) $\begin{array}{r} 337 \\ +262 \\ \hline \end{array}$ 11) $\begin{array}{r} 353 \\ +301 \\ \hline \end{array}$ 12) $\begin{array}{r} 522 \\ +112 \\ \hline \end{array}$

13) $\begin{array}{r} 237 \\ +661 \\ \hline \end{array}$ 14) $\begin{array}{r} 704 \\ +275 \\ \hline \end{array}$ 15) $\begin{array}{r} 152 \\ +641 \\ \hline \end{array}$ 16) $\begin{array}{r} 274 \\ +501 \\ \hline \end{array}$

3 Digit Addition No Regrouping

Add.

1)   472
    +127
    _____

2)   413
    +281
    _____

3)   229
    +540
    _____

4)   534
    +350
    _____

5)   261
    +123
    _____

6)   337
    +350
    _____

7)   318
    +651
    _____

8)   301
    +613
    _____

9)   254
    +522
    _____

10) 501
    +335
    _____

11) 415
    +353
    _____

12) 520
    +414
    _____

13) 303
    +170
    _____

14) 120
    +335
    _____

15) 102
    +104
    _____

16) 130
    +153
    _____

3 Digit Addition   No Regrouping

Add.

1) 665
   +211

2) 125
   +561

3) 396
   +102

4) 422
   +427

5) 415
   +472

6) 526
   +261

7) 260
   +623

8) 142
   +246

9) 183
   +204

10) 408
    +340

11) 199
    +800

12) 202
    +340

13) 480
    +102

14) 620
    +307

15) 123
    +224

16) 822
    +164

Name _____ Date _____

3 Digit Addition No Regrouping

Add.

1) $\begin{array}{r} 732 \\ +204 \\ \hline \end{array}$ 2) $\begin{array}{r} 131 \\ +667 \\ \hline \end{array}$ 3) $\begin{array}{r} 617 \\ +210 \\ \hline \end{array}$ 4) $\begin{array}{r} 321 \\ +572 \\ \hline \end{array}$

5) $\begin{array}{r} 438 \\ +200 \\ \hline \end{array}$ 6) $\begin{array}{r} 201 \\ +611 \\ \hline \end{array}$ 7) $\begin{array}{r} 215 \\ +281 \\ \hline \end{array}$ 8) $\begin{array}{r} 706 \\ +233 \\ \hline \end{array}$

9) $\begin{array}{r} 354 \\ +524 \\ \hline \end{array}$ 10) $\begin{array}{r} 503 \\ +444 \\ \hline \end{array}$ 11) $\begin{array}{r} 740 \\ +122 \\ \hline \end{array}$ 12) $\begin{array}{r} 641 \\ +343 \\ \hline \end{array}$

13) $\begin{array}{r} 607 \\ +100 \\ \hline \end{array}$ 14) $\begin{array}{r} 124 \\ +421 \\ \hline \end{array}$ 15) $\begin{array}{r} 142 \\ +334 \\ \hline \end{array}$ 16) $\begin{array}{r} 335 \\ +622 \\ \hline \end{array}$

www.claymaze.com

3 Digit Addition   No Regrouping

Add.

1)   474
    +401

2)   146
    +623

3)   367
    +122

4)   655
    +133

5)   407
    +232

6)   177
    +420

7)   212
    +335

8)   231
    +757

9)   450
    +533

10) 207
    +281

11) 751
    +226

12) 612
    +186

13) 294
    +403

14) 374
    +103

15) 306
    +173

16) 124
    +364

3 Digit Addition No Regrouping

Add.

1) 102
   +510

2) 640
   +235

3) 316
   +460

4) 344
   +534

5) 305
   +502

6) 331
   +650

7) 566
   +313

8) 760
   +221

9) 604
   +211

10) 601
    +171

11) 170
    +117

12) 217
    +650

13) 281
    +514

14) 109
    +840

15) 276
    +522

16) 481
    +210

www.claymaze.com

3 Digit Addition | No Regrouping

Add.

1) 259
   +400
   ‾‾‾‾‾

2) 365
   +222
   ‾‾‾‾‾

3) 431
   +163
   ‾‾‾‾‾

4) 273
   +513
   ‾‾‾‾‾

5) 607
   +220
   ‾‾‾‾‾

6) 574
   +320
   ‾‾‾‾‾

7) 318
   +100
   ‾‾‾‾‾

8) 241
   +721
   ‾‾‾‾‾

9) 639
   +240
   ‾‾‾‾‾

10) 550
   +103
   ‾‾‾‾‾

11) 714
   +150
   ‾‾‾‾‾

12) 163
   +225
   ‾‾‾‾‾

13) 346
   +200
   ‾‾‾‾‾

14) 326
   +221
   ‾‾‾‾‾

15) 260
   +103
   ‾‾‾‾‾

16) 752
   +220
   ‾‾‾‾‾

3 Digit Addition No Regrouping

Add.

1) $\begin{array}{r} 754 \\ +120 \\ \hline \end{array}$ 2) $\begin{array}{r} 897 \\ +100 \\ \hline \end{array}$ 3) $\begin{array}{r} 610 \\ +343 \\ \hline \end{array}$ 4) $\begin{array}{r} 520 \\ +154 \\ \hline \end{array}$

5) $\begin{array}{r} 541 \\ +451 \\ \hline \end{array}$ 6) $\begin{array}{r} 612 \\ +275 \\ \hline \end{array}$ 7) $\begin{array}{r} 221 \\ +216 \\ \hline \end{array}$ 8) $\begin{array}{r} 421 \\ +167 \\ \hline \end{array}$

9) $\begin{array}{r} 120 \\ +678 \\ \hline \end{array}$ 10) $\begin{array}{r} 273 \\ +310 \\ \hline \end{array}$ 11) $\begin{array}{r} 323 \\ +415 \\ \hline \end{array}$ 12) $\begin{array}{r} 145 \\ +343 \\ \hline \end{array}$

13) $\begin{array}{r} 680 \\ +116 \\ \hline \end{array}$ 14) $\begin{array}{r} 313 \\ +680 \\ \hline \end{array}$ 15) $\begin{array}{r} 501 \\ +252 \\ \hline \end{array}$ 16) $\begin{array}{r} 271 \\ +207 \\ \hline \end{array}$

3 Digit Addition | No Regrouping

Add.

1) 103
   +473

2) 331
   +561

3) 517
   +260

4) 467
   +332

5) 860
   +139

6) 205
   +203

7) 270
   +707

8) 372
   +525

9) 291
   +103

10) 471
   +215

11) 230
   +534

12) 512
   +351

13) 223
   +174

14) 362
   +302

15) 506
   +390

16) 544
   +231

3 Digit Addition No Regrouping

Add.

1)   201
   +200

2)   741
   +142

3)   250
   +342

4)   430
   +314

5)   414
   +275

6)   133
   +853

7)   304
   +133

8)   431
   +365

9)   260
   +629

10)   641
   +312

11)   282
   +217

12)   157
   +201

13)   153
   +401

14)   651
   +333

15)   480
   +216

16)   510
   +482

3 Digit Addition   No Regrouping

Add.

1) 112
   +417

2) 242
   +715

3) 800
   +190

4) 276
   +402

5) 605
   +320

6) 115
   +571

7) 134
   +765

8) 230
   +706

9) 532
   +310

10) 791
   +107

11) 801
   +128

12) 450
   +444

13) 410
   +386

14) 284
   +700

15) 415
   +150

16) 674
   +301

SECTION

3-DIGIT
ADDITION
WITH REGROUPING

11 worksheets
16 problems per sheet

3 Digit Addition With Regrouping

Add.

1) $\begin{array}{r} 386 \\ +492 \\ \hline \end{array}$
2) $\begin{array}{r} 343 \\ +888 \\ \hline \end{array}$
3) $\begin{array}{r} 942 \\ +587 \\ \hline \end{array}$
4) $\begin{array}{r} 552 \\ +783 \\ \hline \end{array}$

5) $\begin{array}{r} 563 \\ +741 \\ \hline \end{array}$
6) $\begin{array}{r} 262 \\ +757 \\ \hline \end{array}$
7) $\begin{array}{r} 123 \\ +629 \\ \hline \end{array}$
8) $\begin{array}{r} 156 \\ +556 \\ \hline \end{array}$

9) $\begin{array}{r} 190 \\ +190 \\ \hline \end{array}$
10) $\begin{array}{r} 970 \\ +370 \\ \hline \end{array}$
11) $\begin{array}{r} 334 \\ +196 \\ \hline \end{array}$
12) $\begin{array}{r} 962 \\ +452 \\ \hline \end{array}$

13) $\begin{array}{r} 179 \\ +638 \\ \hline \end{array}$
14) $\begin{array}{r} 168 \\ +337 \\ \hline \end{array}$
15) $\begin{array}{r} 699 \\ +132 \\ \hline \end{array}$
16) $\begin{array}{r} 225 \\ +308 \\ \hline \end{array}$

3 Digit Addition With Regrouping

Add.

1)   185
   +218

2)   987
   +809

3)   451
   +667

4)   486
   +874

5)   651
   +656

6)   891
   +576

7)   943
   +176

8)   166
   +608

9)   386
   +955

10)   586
   +272

11)   284
   +960

12)   209
   +441

13)   272
   +836

14)   245
   +636

15)   434
   +780

16)   554
   +829

3 Digit Addition With Regrouping

Add.

1) 490
   +383

2) 946
   +673

3) 592
   +113

4) 380
   +849

5) 447
   +727

6) 789
   +264

7) 138
   +622

8) 233
   +689

9) 199
   +446

10) 717
    +394

11) 613
    +409

12) 818
    +998

13) 396
    +685

14) 555
    +792

15) 256
    +391

16) 484
    +796

3 Digit Addition With Regrouping

Add.

1) 662
   +577
   ─────

2) 563
   +976
   ─────

3) 297
   +615
   ─────

4) 658
   +636
   ─────

5) 866
   +365
   ─────

6) 945
   +685
   ─────

7) 779
   +648
   ─────

8) 787
   +858
   ─────

9) 796
   +536
   ─────

10) 719
   +902
   ─────

11) 326
   +449
   ─────

12) 824
   +116
   ─────

13) 129
   +361
   ─────

14) 739
   +944
   ─────

15) 513
   +694
   ─────

16) 546
   +885
   ─────

3 Digit Addition With Regrouping

Add.

1) 439
   +518

2) 780
   +586

3) 215
   +256

4) 601
   +779

5) 391
   +922

6) 925
   +466

7) 483
   +719

8) 580
   +254

9) 766
   +181

10) 471
    +684

11) 674
    +181

12) 627
    +205

13) 672
    +661

14) 323
    +295

15) 569
    +816

16) 838
    +405

3 Digit Addition With Regrouping

Add.

1)   275
   +964
   ‾‾‾‾‾

2)   758
   +352
   ‾‾‾‾‾

3)   743
   +593
   ‾‾‾‾‾

4)   968
   +387
   ‾‾‾‾‾

5)   164
   +999
   ‾‾‾‾‾

6)   185
   +370
   ‾‾‾‾‾

7)   974
   +696
   ‾‾‾‾‾

8)   674
   +498
   ‾‾‾‾‾

9)   155
   +827
   ‾‾‾‾‾

10)   593
    +456
    ‾‾‾‾‾

11)   551
    +154
    ‾‾‾‾‾

12)   250
    +665
    ‾‾‾‾‾

13)   446
    +675
    ‾‾‾‾‾

14)   404
    +197
    ‾‾‾‾‾

15)   374
    +337
    ‾‾‾‾‾

16)   465
    +375
    ‾‾‾‾‾

3 Digit Addition | With Regrouping

Add.

1) 292
   +269

2) 218
   +119

3) 753
   +183

4) 758
   +175

5) 319
   +292

6) 870
   +280

7) 899
   +812

8) 694
   +337

9) 994
   +618

10) 638
    +563

11) 393
    +270

12) 238
    +218

13) 441
    +792

14) 293
    +986

15) 846
    +381

16) 786
    +775

www.claymaze.com

3 Digit Addition With Regrouping

Add.

1) $\begin{array}{r} 125 \\ +618 \\ \hline \end{array}$ 2) $\begin{array}{r} 499 \\ +524 \\ \hline \end{array}$ 3) $\begin{array}{r} 740 \\ +382 \\ \hline \end{array}$ 4) $\begin{array}{r} 145 \\ +369 \\ \hline \end{array}$

5) $\begin{array}{r} 181 \\ +741 \\ \hline \end{array}$ 6) $\begin{array}{r} 262 \\ +440 \\ \hline \end{array}$ 7) $\begin{array}{r} 595 \\ +907 \\ \hline \end{array}$ 8) $\begin{array}{r} 684 \\ +727 \\ \hline \end{array}$

9) $\begin{array}{r} 194 \\ +511 \\ \hline \end{array}$ 10) $\begin{array}{r} 768 \\ +404 \\ \hline \end{array}$ 11) $\begin{array}{r} 517 \\ +754 \\ \hline \end{array}$ 12) $\begin{array}{r} 374 \\ +483 \\ \hline \end{array}$

13) $\begin{array}{r} 808 \\ +894 \\ \hline \end{array}$ 14) $\begin{array}{r} 236 \\ +318 \\ \hline \end{array}$ 15) $\begin{array}{r} 523 \\ +137 \\ \hline \end{array}$ 16) $\begin{array}{r} 874 \\ +252 \\ \hline \end{array}$

www.claymaze.com

Name _____   Date _____

3 Digit Addition   With Regrouping

Add.

1) $\begin{array}{r} 707 \\ +804 \\ \hline \end{array}$
2) $\begin{array}{r} 105 \\ +228 \\ \hline \end{array}$
3) $\begin{array}{r} 868 \\ +203 \\ \hline \end{array}$
4) $\begin{array}{r} 772 \\ +262 \\ \hline \end{array}$

5) $\begin{array}{r} 149 \\ +809 \\ \hline \end{array}$
6) $\begin{array}{r} 768 \\ +196 \\ \hline \end{array}$
7) $\begin{array}{r} 208 \\ +795 \\ \hline \end{array}$
8) $\begin{array}{r} 630 \\ +676 \\ \hline \end{array}$

9) $\begin{array}{r} 455 \\ +582 \\ \hline \end{array}$
10) $\begin{array}{r} 502 \\ +798 \\ \hline \end{array}$
11) $\begin{array}{r} 696 \\ +617 \\ \hline \end{array}$
12) $\begin{array}{r} 860 \\ +753 \\ \hline \end{array}$

13) $\begin{array}{r} 781 \\ +866 \\ \hline \end{array}$
14) $\begin{array}{r} 714 \\ +759 \\ \hline \end{array}$
15) $\begin{array}{r} 258 \\ +786 \\ \hline \end{array}$
16) $\begin{array}{r} 140 \\ +168 \\ \hline \end{array}$

www.claymaze.com

3 Digit Addition — With Regrouping

Add.

1)   293
  +960

2)   203
  +797

3)   691
  +911

4)   235
  +735

5)   381
  +578

6)   428
  +299

7)   858
  +328

8)   121
  +209

9)   558
  +167

10)   585
  +481

11)   299
  +281

12)   399
  +111

13)   334
  +107

14)   648
  +267

15)   628
  +808

16)   985
  +243

3 Digit Addition | With Regrouping

Add.

1) 710
   +293

2) 118
   +232

3) 232
   +872

4) 472
   +184

5) 230
   +274

6) 444
   +858

7) 676
   +835

8) 682
   +765

9) 193
   +839

10) 483
    +662

11) 492
    +860

12) 373
    +863

13) 908
    +318

14) 576
    +246

15) 392
    +853

16) 496
    +489

SECTION

9

3-DIGIT SUBTRACTION
NO REGROUPING

11 worksheets
16 problems per sheet

3 Digit Subtraction No Regrouping

Subtract.

1) 148
   -102

2) 126
   -113

3) 298
   -148

4) 387
   -343

5) 149
   -137

6) 123
   -102

7) 695
   -253

8) 798
   -130

9) 598
   -535

10) 769
   -554

11) 464
   -141

12) 390
   -310

13) 839
   -316

14) 452
   -330

15) 445
   -411

16) 860
   -230

3 Digit Subtraction No Regrouping

Subtract.

1) 587
   −534
   ‾‾‾‾‾

2) 597
   −120
   ‾‾‾‾‾

3) 133
   −102
   ‾‾‾‾‾

4) 143
   −113
   ‾‾‾‾‾

5) 588
   −453
   ‾‾‾‾‾

6) 564
   −412
   ‾‾‾‾‾

7) 155
   −130
   ‾‾‾‾‾

8) 478
   −201
   ‾‾‾‾‾

9) 515
   −501
   ‾‾‾‾‾

10) 268
    −150
    ‾‾‾‾‾

11) 974
    −502
    ‾‾‾‾‾

12) 746
    −315
    ‾‾‾‾‾

13) 487
    −327
    ‾‾‾‾‾

14) 865
    −202
    ‾‾‾‾‾

15) 878
    −806
    ‾‾‾‾‾

16) 849
    −527
    ‾‾‾‾‾

www.claymaze.com

3 Digit Subtraction   No Regrouping

Subtract.

1)   959
   − 616

2)   743
   − 512

3)   152
   − 102

4)   794
   − 264

5)   248
   − 204

6)   660
   − 440

7)   777
   − 737

8)   139
   − 124

9)   179
   − 160

10)   734
   − 613

11)   187
   − 150

12)   880
   − 220

13)   898
   − 450

14)   948
   − 404

15)   597
   − 362

16)   469
   − 415

3 Digit Subtraction No Regrouping

Subtract.

1)   969
   − 317

2)   967
   − 242

3)   299
   − 262

4)   366
   − 322

5)   681
   − 140

6)   164
   − 152

7)   576
   − 254

8)   337
   − 312

9)   399
   − 114

10)   949
    − 105

11)   778
    − 518

12)   288
    − 214

13)   921
    − 911

14)   496
    − 464

15)   146
    − 133

16)   766
    − 634

3 Digit Subtraction No Regrouping

Subtract.

1)   954
   -814

2)   982
   -400

3)   747
   -727

4)   160
   -150

5)   197
   -183

6)   494
   -300

7)   242
   -202

8)   453
   -443

9)   727
   -700

10)   349
   -139

11)   658
   -142

12)   119
   -103

13)   273
   -213

14)   259
   -215

15)   988
   -764

16)   521
   -310

3 Digit Subtraction   No Regrouping

Subtract.

1)   197
   − 167

2)   354
   − 130

3)   863
   − 732

4)   128
   − 110

5)   597
   − 537

6)   972
   − 260

7)   189
   − 100

8)   299
   − 178

9)   697
   − 453

10)   947
   − 223

11)   819
   − 809

12)   117
   − 107

13)   888
   − 605

14)   286
   − 202

15)   187
   − 121

16)   878
   − 306

3 Digit Subtraction No Regrouping

Subtract.

1) 393
  − 352

2) 167
  − 150

3) 248
  − 132

4) 758
  − 535

5) 227
  − 114

6) 859
  − 502

7) 549
  − 335

8) 279
  − 121

9) 499
  − 327

10) 596
   − 154

11) 263
   − 233

12) 251
   − 130

13) 631
   − 400

14) 589
   − 116

15) 157
   − 112

16) 757
   − 326

www.claymaze.com

3 Digit Subtraction — No Regrouping

Subtract.

1) 391
   −101
   ——

2) 787
   −742
   ——

3) 749
   −112
   ——

4) 596
   −284
   ——

5) 177
   −167
   ——

6) 646
   −135
   ——

7) 896
   −616
   ——

8) 936
   −720
   ——

9) 274
   −252
   ——

10) 986
    −430
    ——

11) 894
    −551
    ——

12) 597
    −232
    ——

13) 979
    −644
    ——

14) 796
    −502
    ——

15) 489
    −412
    ——

16) 726
    −500
    ——

3 Digit Subtraction   No Regrouping

Subtract.

1) 956
   -636

2) 399
   -344

3) 980
   -410

4) 988
   -558

5) 281
   -260

6) 134
   -112

7) 492
   -241

8) 698
   -336

9) 296
   -143

10) 229
   -217

11) 878
   -504

12) 136
   -101

13) 285
   -162

14) 380
   -270

15) 669
   -334

16) 293
   -240

3 Digit Subtraction No Regrouping

Subtract.

1)   188
   − 147
   _____

2)   127
   − 105
   _____

3)   867
   − 241
   _____

4)   645
   − 211
   _____

5)   992
   − 481
   _____

6)   126
   − 105
   _____

7)   797
   − 744
   _____

8)   374
   − 153
   _____

9)   792
   − 541
   _____

10)   249
   − 223
   _____

11)   174
   − 103
   _____

12)   377
   − 346
   _____

13)   584
   − 274
   _____

14)   475
   − 451
   _____

15)   367
   − 331
   _____

16)   274
   − 263
   _____

3 Digit Subtraction   No Regrouping

Subtract.

1)   878
    -707

2)   334
    -320

3)   975
    -552

4)   786
    -654

5)   633
    -222

6)   267
    -237

7)   788
    -201

8)   516
    -203

9)   357
    -140

10) 518
    -104

11) 699
    -468

12) 656
    -616

13) 287
    -244

14) 338
    -217

15) 781
    -570

16) 196
    -102

SECTION

3-DIGIT SUBTRACTION
WITH REGROUPING

11 worksheets
16 problems per sheet

3 Digit Subtraction   With Regrouping

Subtract.

1) 262
   -239
   ____

2) 180
   -126
   ____

3) 990
   -233
   ____

4) 791
   -768
   ____

5) 417
   -154
   ____

6) 828
   -490
   ____

7) 647
   -186
   ____

8) 315
   -228
   ____

9) 445
   -255
   ____

10) 472
   -397
   ____

11) 221
   -136
   ____

12) 535
   -344
   ____

13) 845
   -479
   ____

14) 515
   -167
   ____

15) 230
   -171
   ____

16) 872
   -513
   ____

3 Digit Subtraction — With Regrouping

Subtract.

1) 712
   − 259

2) 316
   − 235

3) 790
   − 552

4) 784
   − 487

5) 582
   − 466

6) 271
   − 263

7) 845
   − 574

8) 572
   − 527

9) 985
   − 778

10) 352
    − 199

11) 807
    − 246

12) 225
    − 177

13) 248
    − 171

14) 829
    − 651

15) 996
    − 599

16) 430
    − 358

3 Digit Subtraction | With Regrouping

Subtract.

1)   565
   − 183

2)   383
   − 247

3)   573
   − 188

4)   920
   − 274

5)   508
   − 290

6)   191
   − 137

7)   501
   − 386

8)   502
   − 449

9)   467
   − 277

10)   318
   − 246

11)   686
   − 478

12)   634
   − 147

13)   923
   − 497

14)   434
   − 384

15)   325
   − 262

16)   253
   − 172

3 Digit Subtraction With Regrouping

Subtract.

1)   352
   − 338
   ———

2)   964
   − 367
   ———

3)   252
   − 154
   ———

4)   501
   − 205
   ———

5)   528
   − 362
   ———

6)   692
   − 627
   ———

7)   343
   − 148
   ———

8)   727
   − 537
   ———

9)   591
   − 283
   ———

10)   451
   − 389
   ———

11)   571
   − 559
   ———

12)   736
   − 647
   ———

13)   928
   − 387
   ———

14)   203
   − 193
   ———

15)   960
   − 387
   ———

16)   625
   − 386
   ———

3 Digit Subtraction With Regrouping

Subtract.

1) 415
  - 188

2) 623
  - 561

3) 170
  - 135

4) 626
  - 588

5) 586
  - 348

6) 426
  - 365

7) 766
  - 457

8) 851
  - 423

9) 520
  - 247

10) 940
   - 697

11) 538
   - 378

12) 653
   - 447

13) 882
   - 713

14) 302
   - 115

15) 611
   - 415

16) 397
   - 338

3 Digit Subtraction With Regrouping

Subtract.

1) 120
   -105
   ─────

2) 902
   -348
   ─────

3) 834
   -746
   ─────

4) 723
   -532
   ─────

5) 323
   -105
   ─────

6) 141
   -108
   ─────

7) 687
   -379
   ─────

8) 161
   -105
   ─────

9) 265
   -179
   ─────

10) 278
   -180
   ─────

11) 770
   -508
   ─────

12) 792
   -409
   ─────

13) 164
   -146
   ─────

14) 230
   -145
   ─────

15) 244
   -117
   ─────

16) 492
   -343
   ─────

3 Digit Subtraction | With Regrouping

Subtract.

1) 901
  − 821

2) 920
  − 193

3) 816
  − 567

4) 419
  − 294

5) 693
  − 645

6) 609
  − 535

7) 925
  − 139

8) 791
  − 749

9) 835
  − 644

10) 688
   − 339

11) 903
   − 213

12) 965
   − 697

13) 422
   − 288

14) 304
   − 139

15) 481
   − 392

16) 794
   − 196

www.claymaze.com

3 Digit Subtraction — With Regrouping

Subtract.

1)   833
   − 465
   _____

2)   608
   − 161
   _____

3)   326
   − 129
   _____

4)   956
   − 527
   _____

5)   342
   − 117
   _____

6)   670
   − 644
   _____

7)   182
   − 166
   _____

8)   240
   − 152
   _____

9)   337
   − 280
   _____

10)   802
    − 133
    _____

11)   491
    − 458
    _____

12)   944
    − 536
    _____

13)   648
    − 480
    _____

14)   286
    − 119
    _____

15)   365
    − 196
    _____

16)   784
    − 178
    _____

3 Digit Subtraction   With Regrouping

Subtract.

1)   739
    −652

2)   171
    −103

3)   205
    −125

4)   303
    −187

5)   140
    −112

6)   620
    −403

7)   975
    −158

8)   943
    −868

9)   536
    −271

10) 858
    −581

11) 292
    −167

12) 560
    −375

13) 214
    −161

14) 696
    −187

15) 564
    −157

16) 809
    −717

3 Digit Subtraction With Regrouping

Subtract.

1) $\begin{array}{r} 729 \\ -246 \\ \hline \end{array}$ 2) $\begin{array}{r} 562 \\ -508 \\ \hline \end{array}$ 3) $\begin{array}{r} 970 \\ -583 \\ \hline \end{array}$ 4) $\begin{array}{r} 830 \\ -596 \\ \hline \end{array}$

5) $\begin{array}{r} 781 \\ -503 \\ \hline \end{array}$ 6) $\begin{array}{r} 431 \\ -207 \\ \hline \end{array}$ 7) $\begin{array}{r} 541 \\ -456 \\ \hline \end{array}$ 8) $\begin{array}{r} 400 \\ -362 \\ \hline \end{array}$

9) $\begin{array}{r} 989 \\ -697 \\ \hline \end{array}$ 10) $\begin{array}{r} 306 \\ -210 \\ \hline \end{array}$ 11) $\begin{array}{r} 722 \\ -636 \\ \hline \end{array}$ 12) $\begin{array}{r} 309 \\ -289 \\ \hline \end{array}$

13) $\begin{array}{r} 706 \\ -399 \\ \hline \end{array}$ 14) $\begin{array}{r} 605 \\ -516 \\ \hline \end{array}$ 15) $\begin{array}{r} 913 \\ -233 \\ \hline \end{array}$ 16) $\begin{array}{r} 941 \\ -639 \\ \hline \end{array}$

www.claymaze.com

3 Digit Subtraction   With Regrouping

Subtract.

1)
$$\begin{array}{r} 625 \\ -231 \\ \hline \end{array}$$

2)
$$\begin{array}{r} 372 \\ -281 \\ \hline \end{array}$$

3)
$$\begin{array}{r} 833 \\ -537 \\ \hline \end{array}$$

4)
$$\begin{array}{r} 922 \\ -369 \\ \hline \end{array}$$

5)
$$\begin{array}{r} 618 \\ -123 \\ \hline \end{array}$$

6)
$$\begin{array}{r} 425 \\ -157 \\ \hline \end{array}$$

7)
$$\begin{array}{r} 707 \\ -435 \\ \hline \end{array}$$

8)
$$\begin{array}{r} 989 \\ -897 \\ \hline \end{array}$$

9)
$$\begin{array}{r} 677 \\ -378 \\ \hline \end{array}$$

10)
$$\begin{array}{r} 646 \\ -208 \\ \hline \end{array}$$

11)
$$\begin{array}{r} 245 \\ -206 \\ \hline \end{array}$$

12)
$$\begin{array}{r} 135 \\ -128 \\ \hline \end{array}$$

13)
$$\begin{array}{r} 691 \\ -667 \\ \hline \end{array}$$

14)
$$\begin{array}{r} 914 \\ -808 \\ \hline \end{array}$$

15)
$$\begin{array}{r} 708 \\ -410 \\ \hline \end{array}$$

16)
$$\begin{array}{r} 161 \\ -147 \\ \hline \end{array}$$

www.claymaze.com

SECTION

2-DIGIT, 3-ADDEND STACK ADDITION

11 worksheets
12 problems per sheet

2 Digit Addition | Adding 3 Numbers

Add.

1)
```
  59
  63
+ 90
```

2)
```
  56
  11
+ 30
```

3)
```
  35
  52
+ 11
```

4)
```
  61
  33
+ 29
```

5)
```
  27
  57
+ 20
```

6)
```
  98
  27
+ 37
```

7)
```
  10
  43
+ 25
```

8)
```
  38
  29
+ 26
```

9)
```
  30
  79
+ 65
```

10)
```
  41
  93
+ 46
```

11)
```
  58
  43
+ 45
```

12)
```
  48
  83
+ 28
```

2 Digit Addition — Adding 3 Numbers

Add.

1)   14
     54
 + 37
	2) 45
	     52
	 + 14
		3) 35
		     81
		 + 17
			4) 70
			     60
			 + 27

5)   54
     18
 + 54
	6) 15
	     79
	 + 57
		7) 91
		     43
		 + 58
			8) 72
			     24
			 + 62

9)   87
     83
 + 17
	10) 69
	     42
	 + 64
		11) 13
		     17
		 + 19
			12) 86
			     83
			 + 72

2 Digit Addition   Adding 3 Numbers

Add.

1) $\begin{array}{r} 77 \\ 23 \\ +76 \\ \hline \end{array}$

2) $\begin{array}{r} 95 \\ 68 \\ +49 \\ \hline \end{array}$

3) $\begin{array}{r} 14 \\ 28 \\ +32 \\ \hline \end{array}$

4) $\begin{array}{r} 25 \\ 99 \\ +43 \\ \hline \end{array}$

5) $\begin{array}{r} 34 \\ 70 \\ +12 \\ \hline \end{array}$

6) $\begin{array}{r} 58 \\ 94 \\ +80 \\ \hline \end{array}$

7) $\begin{array}{r} 21 \\ 37 \\ +95 \\ \hline \end{array}$

8) $\begin{array}{r} 86 \\ 77 \\ +78 \\ \hline \end{array}$

9) $\begin{array}{r} 59 \\ 75 \\ +88 \\ \hline \end{array}$

10) $\begin{array}{r} 56 \\ 49 \\ +77 \\ \hline \end{array}$

11) $\begin{array}{r} 67 \\ 85 \\ +78 \\ \hline \end{array}$

12) $\begin{array}{r} 98 \\ 77 \\ +52 \\ \hline \end{array}$

2 Digit Addition Adding 3 Numbers

Add.

1) 37
    35
  + 29
  ‾‾‾‾

2) 27
    13
  + 69
  ‾‾‾‾

3) 36
    88
  + 11
  ‾‾‾‾

4) 17
    47
  + 49
  ‾‾‾‾

5) 74
    67
  + 82
  ‾‾‾‾

6) 77
    18
  + 92
  ‾‾‾‾

7) 25
    22
  + 66
  ‾‾‾‾

8) 10
    77
  + 51
  ‾‾‾‾

9) 56
    31
  + 14
  ‾‾‾‾

10) 58
    57
  + 88
  ‾‾‾‾

11) 42
    67
  + 42
  ‾‾‾‾

12) 92
    27
  + 94
  ‾‾‾‾

2 Digit Addition Adding 3 Numbers

Add.

1)
```
   75
   52
 + 82
 ----
```

2)
```
   69
   32
 + 68
 ----
```

3)
```
   58
   82
 + 20
 ----
```

4)
```
   17
   23
 + 82
 ----
```

5)
```
   35
   42
 + 43
 ----
```

6)
```
   11
   31
 + 63
 ----
```

7)
```
   47
   35
 + 94
 ----
```

8)
```
   42
   11
 + 94
 ----
```

9)
```
   86
   77
 + 43
 ----
```

10)
```
   95
   43
 + 28
 ----
```

11)
```
   39
   73
 + 37
 ----
```

12)
```
   77
   31
 + 17
 ----
```

2 Digit Addition Adding 3 Numbers

Add.

1)
```
   6 5
   8 1
 + 5 9
 _____
```

2)
```
   7 3
   1 5
 + 6 5
 _____
```

3)
```
   7 8
   3 0
 + 8 8
 _____
```

4)
```
   9 6
   9 6
 + 7 2
 _____
```

5)
```
   6 9
   5 8
 + 5 4
 _____
```

6)
```
   6 0
   5 7
 + 6 0
 _____
```

7)
```
   2 7
   8 1
 + 1 4
 _____
```

8)
```
   7 7
   4 8
 + 8 8
 _____
```

9)
```
   3 9
   4 0
 + 1 2
 _____
```

10)
```
   7 9
   9 5
 + 1 2
 _____
```

11)
```
   4 0
   9 4
 + 1 1
 _____
```

12)
```
   1 3
   2 7
 + 4 1
 _____
```

2 Digit Addition   Adding 3 Numbers

Add.

1)
```
   2 0
   3 2
 + 5 7
 ------
```

2)
```
   4 4
   3 7
 + 7 0
 ------
```

3)
```
   3 7
   1 6
 + 1 0
 ------
```

4)
```
   3 1
   2 8
 + 3 8
 ------
```

5)
```
   8 2
   6 9
 + 6 0
 ------
```

6)
```
   6 3
   8 1
 + 2 4
 ------
```

7)
```
   2 9
   8 8
 + 6 1
 ------
```

8)
```
   5 1
   5 6
 + 6 5
 ------
```

9)
```
   7 9
   3 7
 + 8 2
 ------
```

10)
```
   4 3
   8 3
 + 9 3
 ------
```

11)
```
   8 9
   1 6
 + 8 2
 ------
```

12)
```
   8 5
   9 4
 + 5 2
 ------
```

2 Digit Addition | Adding 3 Numbers

Add.

1)
```
   6 4
   3 4
 + 4 6
 _____
```

2)
```
   7 2
   5 0
 + 6 6
 _____
```

3)
```
   5 3
   9 9
 + 5 8
 _____
```

4)
```
   2 5
   8 1
 + 7 8
 _____
```

5)
```
   2 9
   4 2
 + 4 7
 _____
```

6)
```
   3 1
   3 8
 + 2 5
 _____
```

7)
```
   9 5
   2 2
 + 2 7
 _____
```

8)
```
   1 7
   5 4
 + 7 0
 _____
```

9)
```
   7 1
   1 4
 + 6 7
 _____
```

10)
```
   6 1
   2 1
 + 5 9
 _____
```

11)
```
   5 2
   1 3
 + 4 3
 _____
```

12)
```
   5 9
   6 3
 + 8 2
 _____
```

2 Digit Addition   Adding 3 Numbers

Add.

1)   44
     40
  + 71
  _____

2)   27
     91
  + 37
  _____

3)   28
     98
  + 30
  _____

4)   65
     85
  + 52
  _____

5)   85
     43
  + 80
  _____

6)   56
     72
  + 25
  _____

7)   80
     51
  + 33
  _____

8)   18
     14
  + 22
  _____

9)   57
     77
  + 36
  _____

10) 91
     94
  + 29
  _____

11) 76
     64
  + 52
  _____

12) 19
     61
  + 63
  _____

2 Digit Addition Adding 3 Numbers

Add.

1)
```
   68
   57
 + 90
 ____
```

2)
```
   52
   90
 + 55
 ____
```

3)
```
   56
   36
 + 88
 ____
```

4)
```
   38
   13
 + 71
 ____
```

5)
```
   82
   83
 + 48
 ____
```

6)
```
   31
   46
 + 39
 ____
```

7)
```
   25
   13
 + 90
 ____
```

8)
```
   73
   29
 + 73
 ____
```

9)
```
   98
   36
 + 13
 ____
```

10)
```
   37
   92
 + 93
 ____
```

11)
```
   65
   49
 + 44
 ____
```

12)
```
   96
   46
 + 29
 ____
```

2 Digit Addition   Adding 3 Numbers

Add.

1)   13
     84
   + 70
   ‾‾‾‾‾

2)   85
     76
   + 25
   ‾‾‾‾‾

3)   86
     81
   + 62
   ‾‾‾‾‾

4)   39
     31
   + 71
   ‾‾‾‾‾

5)   60
     90
   + 58
   ‾‾‾‾‾

6)   84
     21
   + 97
   ‾‾‾‾‾

7)   98
     19
   + 32
   ‾‾‾‾‾

8)   22
     35
   + 84
   ‾‾‾‾‾

9)   46
     55
   + 69
   ‾‾‾‾‾

10)   87
      60
    + 69
    ‾‾‾‾‾

11)   58
      25
    + 72
    ‾‾‾‾‾

12)   11
      73
    + 30
    ‾‾‾‾‾

SECTION

3-DIGIT SUBTRACTION
REGROUPING with 0's

11 worksheets
16 problems per sheet

3 Digit Subtraction   Regrouping with 0's

Subtract.

1)   300
   −154

2)   900
   −495

3)   400
   −105

4)   400
   −222

5)   400
   −388

6)   500
   −276

7)   700
   −596

8)   600
   −516

9)   500
   −202

10)   600
    −447

11)   600
    −336

12)   700
    −479

13)   900
    −649

14)   700
    −319

15)   800
    −357

16)   600
    −156

3 Digit Subtraction — Regrouping with 0's

Subtract.

1) $400 - 322$

2) $900 - 224$

3) $500 - 289$

4) $400 - 171$

5) $200 - 146$

6) $800 - 351$

7) $600 - 175$

8) $400 - 324$

9) $900 - 526$

10) $600 - 158$

11) $400 - 121$

12) $700 - 512$

13) $700 - 538$

14) $300 - 136$

15) $300 - 297$

16) $300 - 262$

3 Digit Subtraction | Regrouping with 0's

Subtract.

1)   200
    −113

2)   500
    −304

3)   700
    −255

4)   400
    −232

5)   400
    −354

6)   400
    −322

7)   700
    −461

8)   800
    −717

9)   700
    −548

10)   400
    −120

11)   200
    −158

12)   600
    −373

13)   900
    −262

14)   600
    −472

15)   200
    −109

16)   500
    −351

3 Digit Subtraction Regrouping with 0's

Subtract.

1) 900
   −735
   ─────

2) 400
   −189
   ─────

3) 200
   −164
   ─────

4) 700
   −615
   ─────

5) 600
   −338
   ─────

6) 700
   −230
   ─────

7) 700
   −569
   ─────

8) 700
   −453
   ─────

9) 400
   −257
   ─────

10) 300
    −239
    ─────

11) 700
    −202
    ─────

12) 300
    −250
    ─────

13) 800
    −583
    ─────

14) 400
    −243
    ─────

15) 900
    −541
    ─────

16) 800
    −162
    ─────

3 Digit Subtraction | Regrouping with 0's

Subtract.

1) 800
   -607

2) 700
   -647

3) 500
   -276

4) 400
   -205

5) 300
   -131

6) 800
   -509

7) 700
   -302

8) 300
   -267

9) 700
   -672

10) 900
   -748

11) 600
   -338

12) 400
   -323

13) 900
   -795

14) 900
   -373

15) 600
   -403

16) 700
   -598

3 Digit Subtraction | Regrouping with 0's

Subtract.

1) $\begin{array}{r} 400 \\ -237 \\ \hline \end{array}$
2) $\begin{array}{r} 500 \\ -427 \\ \hline \end{array}$
3) $\begin{array}{r} 900 \\ -413 \\ \hline \end{array}$
4) $\begin{array}{r} 200 \\ -123 \\ \hline \end{array}$

5) $\begin{array}{r} 500 \\ -430 \\ \hline \end{array}$
6) $\begin{array}{r} 800 \\ -748 \\ \hline \end{array}$
7) $\begin{array}{r} 900 \\ -280 \\ \hline \end{array}$
8) $\begin{array}{r} 200 \\ -115 \\ \hline \end{array}$

9) $\begin{array}{r} 600 \\ -381 \\ \hline \end{array}$
10) $\begin{array}{r} 300 \\ -218 \\ \hline \end{array}$
11) $\begin{array}{r} 500 \\ -221 \\ \hline \end{array}$
12) $\begin{array}{r} 500 \\ -296 \\ \hline \end{array}$

13) $\begin{array}{r} 600 \\ -307 \\ \hline \end{array}$
14) $\begin{array}{r} 400 \\ -268 \\ \hline \end{array}$
15) $\begin{array}{r} 300 \\ -174 \\ \hline \end{array}$
16) $\begin{array}{r} 900 \\ -113 \\ \hline \end{array}$

3 Digit Subtraction Regrouping with 0's

Subtract.

1) $\begin{array}{r} 800 \\ -255 \\ \hline \end{array}$
2) $\begin{array}{r} 200 \\ -185 \\ \hline \end{array}$
3) $\begin{array}{r} 300 \\ -220 \\ \hline \end{array}$
4) $\begin{array}{r} 400 \\ -331 \\ \hline \end{array}$

5) $\begin{array}{r} 700 \\ -468 \\ \hline \end{array}$
6) $\begin{array}{r} 500 \\ -481 \\ \hline \end{array}$
7) $\begin{array}{r} 900 \\ -635 \\ \hline \end{array}$
8) $\begin{array}{r} 900 \\ -795 \\ \hline \end{array}$

9) $\begin{array}{r} 900 \\ -602 \\ \hline \end{array}$
10) $\begin{array}{r} 900 \\ -689 \\ \hline \end{array}$
11) $\begin{array}{r} 600 \\ -330 \\ \hline \end{array}$
12) $\begin{array}{r} 300 \\ -155 \\ \hline \end{array}$

13) $\begin{array}{r} 400 \\ -290 \\ \hline \end{array}$
14) $\begin{array}{r} 700 \\ -521 \\ \hline \end{array}$
15) $\begin{array}{r} 800 \\ -182 \\ \hline \end{array}$
16) $\begin{array}{r} 200 \\ -174 \\ \hline \end{array}$

3 Digit Subtraction | Regrouping with 0's

Subtract.

1) $\begin{array}{r} 600 \\ -291 \\ \hline \end{array}$ 2) $\begin{array}{r} 400 \\ -279 \\ \hline \end{array}$ 3) $\begin{array}{r} 500 \\ -257 \\ \hline \end{array}$ 4) $\begin{array}{r} 300 \\ -101 \\ \hline \end{array}$

5) $\begin{array}{r} 700 \\ -473 \\ \hline \end{array}$ 6) $\begin{array}{r} 700 \\ -202 \\ \hline \end{array}$ 7) $\begin{array}{r} 300 \\ -107 \\ \hline \end{array}$ 8) $\begin{array}{r} 400 \\ -347 \\ \hline \end{array}$

9) $\begin{array}{r} 300 \\ -121 \\ \hline \end{array}$ 10) $\begin{array}{r} 400 \\ -152 \\ \hline \end{array}$ 11) $\begin{array}{r} 700 \\ -577 \\ \hline \end{array}$ 12) $\begin{array}{r} 300 \\ -290 \\ \hline \end{array}$

13) $\begin{array}{r} 900 \\ -562 \\ \hline \end{array}$ 14) $\begin{array}{r} 300 \\ -172 \\ \hline \end{array}$ 15) $\begin{array}{r} 800 \\ -395 \\ \hline \end{array}$ 16) $\begin{array}{r} 700 \\ -175 \\ \hline \end{array}$

Name _____   Date _____

3 Digit Subtraction Regrouping with 0's

Subtract.

1) $\begin{array}{r} 400 \\ -344 \\ \hline \end{array}$

2) $\begin{array}{r} 900 \\ -174 \\ \hline \end{array}$

3) $\begin{array}{r} 700 \\ -256 \\ \hline \end{array}$

4) $\begin{array}{r} 300 \\ -146 \\ \hline \end{array}$

5) $\begin{array}{r} 700 \\ -335 \\ \hline \end{array}$

6) $\begin{array}{r} 400 \\ -205 \\ \hline \end{array}$

7) $\begin{array}{r} 800 \\ -575 \\ \hline \end{array}$

8) $\begin{array}{r} 200 \\ -168 \\ \hline \end{array}$

9) $\begin{array}{r} 900 \\ -171 \\ \hline \end{array}$

10) $\begin{array}{r} 400 \\ -374 \\ \hline \end{array}$

11) $\begin{array}{r} 400 \\ -128 \\ \hline \end{array}$

12) $\begin{array}{r} 300 \\ -159 \\ \hline \end{array}$

13) $\begin{array}{r} 700 \\ -492 \\ \hline \end{array}$

14) $\begin{array}{r} 900 \\ -524 \\ \hline \end{array}$

15) $\begin{array}{r} 700 \\ -247 \\ \hline \end{array}$

16) $\begin{array}{r} 200 \\ -185 \\ \hline \end{array}$

www.claymaze.com

3 Digit Subtraction   Regrouping with 0's

Subtract.

1)   800
   − 684
   _____

2)   900
   − 861
   _____

3)   700
   − 635
   _____

4)   600
   − 137
   _____

5)   200
   − 139
   _____

6)   800
   − 749
   _____

7)   400
   − 334
   _____

8)   600
   − 467
   _____

9)   300
   − 110
   _____

10)   600
   − 204
   _____

11)   200
   − 166
   _____

12)   700
   − 444
   _____

13)   800
   − 507
   _____

14)   700
   − 427
   _____

15)   800
   − 298
   _____

16)   700
   − 305
   _____

3 Digit Subtraction   Regrouping with 0's

Subtract.

1) 800
   -613
   ‾‾‾‾‾

2) 300
   -237
   ‾‾‾‾‾

3) 300
   -180
   ‾‾‾‾‾

4) 400
   -338
   ‾‾‾‾‾

5) 800
   -275
   ‾‾‾‾‾

6) 700
   -328
   ‾‾‾‾‾

7) 200
   -176
   ‾‾‾‾‾

8) 500
   -368
   ‾‾‾‾‾

9) 700
   -630
   ‾‾‾‾‾

10) 200
    -138
   ‾‾‾‾‾

11) 300
    -121
   ‾‾‾‾‾

12) 700
    -537
   ‾‾‾‾‾

13) 300
    -178
   ‾‾‾‾‾

14) 800
    -404
   ‾‾‾‾‾

15) 300
    -140
   ‾‾‾‾‾

16) 700
    -530
   ‾‾‾‾‾

SECTION

FIND
THE MISSING
ADDENDS
ADDITION FACTS

11 worksheets
20 problems per sheet

Find the Missing Addends

Fill in the blanks.

1) $4 + \underline{} = 9$

2) $6 + \underline{} = 11$

3) $6 + \underline{} = 10$

4) $7 + \underline{} = 13$

5) $5 + \underline{} = 7$

6) $4 + \underline{} = 6$

7) $3 + \underline{} = 11$

8) $8 + \underline{} = 9$

9) $6 + \underline{} = 15$

10) $4 + \underline{} = 7$

11) $8 + \underline{} = 14$

12) $7 + \underline{} = 8$

13) $8 + \underline{} = 10$

14) $2 + \underline{} = 3$

15) $3 + \underline{} = 10$

16) $1 + \underline{} = 2$

17) $1 + \underline{} = 5$

18) $5 + \underline{} = 10$

19) $3 + \underline{} = 6$

20) $1 + \underline{} = 4$

Find the Missing Addends

Fill in the blanks.

1) $8 + \underline{} = 17$

2) $2 + \underline{} = 8$

3) $9 + \underline{} = 13$

4) $1 + \underline{} = 5$

5) $6 + \underline{} = 12$

6) $3 + \underline{} = 7$

7) $4 + \underline{} = 8$

8) $6 + \underline{} = 9$

9) $6 + \underline{} = 14$

10) $5 + \underline{} = 13$

11) $9 + \underline{} = 16$

12) $1 + \underline{} = 2$

13) $9 + \underline{} = 12$

14) $4 + \underline{} = 11$

15) $1 + \underline{} = 8$

16) $6 + \underline{} = 11$

17) $1 + \underline{} = 7$

18) $7 + \underline{} = 9$

19) $3 + \underline{} = 8$

20) $6 + \underline{} = 15$

Find the Missing Addends

Fill in the blanks.

1) $4 + \underline{} = 11$

2) $2 + \underline{} = 8$

3) $2 + \underline{} = 10$

4) $6 + \underline{} = 8$

5) $2 + \underline{} = 3$

6) $3 + \underline{} = 7$

7) $6 + \underline{} = 11$

8) $9 + \underline{} = 17$

9) $1 + \underline{} = 6$

10) $8 + \underline{} = 16$

11) $3 + \underline{} = 6$

12) $7 + \underline{} = 10$

13) $5 + \underline{} = 8$

14) $7 + \underline{} = 16$

15) $7 + \underline{} = 12$

16) $4 + \underline{} = 8$

17) $8 + \underline{} = 17$

18) $1 + \underline{} = 4$

19) $8 + \underline{} = 12$

20) $7 + \underline{} = 11$

Find the Missing Addends

Fill in the blanks.

1) $7 + \underline{} = 8$

2) $6 + \underline{} = 11$

3) $6 + \underline{} = 7$

4) $5 + \underline{} = 6$

5) $4 + \underline{} = 8$

6) $2 + \underline{} = 6$

7) $9 + \underline{} = 18$

8) $4 + \underline{} = 7$

9) $7 + \underline{} = 16$

10) $9 + \underline{} = 11$

11) $7 + \underline{} = 14$

12) $4 + \underline{} = 10$

13) $6 + \underline{} = 12$

14) $8 + \underline{} = 16$

15) $9 + \underline{} = 16$

16) $7 + \underline{} = 13$

17) $8 + \underline{} = 17$

18) $8 + \underline{} = 10$

19) $9 + \underline{} = 12$

20) $9 + \underline{} = 10$

www.claymaze.com

Find the Missing Addends

Fill in the blanks.

1) $5 + \underline{} = 9$

2) $8 + \underline{} = 13$

3) $9 + \underline{} = 10$

4) $2 + \underline{} = 6$

5) $6 + \underline{} = 14$

6) $8 + \underline{} = 15$

7) $1 + \underline{} = 5$

8) $1 + \underline{} = 6$

9) $4 + \underline{} = 11$

10) $3 + \underline{} = 9$

11) $5 + \underline{} = 7$

12) $9 + \underline{} = 13$

13) $9 + \underline{} = 17$

14) $6 + \underline{} = 12$

15) $8 + \underline{} = 9$

16) $7 + \underline{} = 15$

17) $4 + \underline{} = 6$

18) $3 + \underline{} = 8$

19) $7 + \underline{} = 12$

20) $5 + \underline{} = 12$

Find the Missing Addends

Fill in the blanks.

1) $6 + \underline{} = 11$

2) $4 + \underline{} = 6$

3) $6 + \underline{} = 15$

4) $3 + \underline{} = 6$

5) $7 + \underline{} = 11$

6) $9 + \underline{} = 18$

7) $5 + \underline{} = 13$

8) $3 + \underline{} = 11$

9) $8 + \underline{} = 17$

10) $4 + \underline{} = 11$

11) $3 + \underline{} = 10$

12) $2 + \underline{} = 4$

13) $6 + \underline{} = 13$

14) $2 + \underline{} = 10$

15) $1 + \underline{} = 5$

16) $2 + \underline{} = 7$

17) $6 + \underline{} = 9$

18) $1 + \underline{} = 9$

19) $7 + \underline{} = 10$

20) $4 + \underline{} = 9$

Find the Missing Addends

Fill in the blanks.

1) $3 + \underline{} = 4$

2) $1 + \underline{} = 8$

3) $1 + \underline{} = 6$

4) $8 + \underline{} = 15$

5) $7 + \underline{} = 10$

6) $4 + \underline{} = 8$

7) $1 + \underline{} = 3$

8) $9 + \underline{} = 13$

9) $3 + \underline{} = 5$

10) $8 + \underline{} = 9$

11) $8 + \underline{} = 13$

12) $9 + \underline{} = 11$

13) $5 + \underline{} = 13$

14) $2 + \underline{} = 8$

15) $8 + \underline{} = 11$

16) $9 + \underline{} = 17$

17) $5 + \underline{} = 11$

18) $8 + \underline{} = 16$

19) $8 + \underline{} = 17$

20) $9 + \underline{} = 10$

Find the Missing Addends

Fill in the blanks.

1) $3 + \underline{\hspace{1cm}} = 6$

2) $7 + \underline{\hspace{1cm}} = 13$

3) $6 + \underline{\hspace{1cm}} = 10$

4) $3 + \underline{\hspace{1cm}} = 7$

5) $4 + \underline{\hspace{1cm}} = 13$

6) $3 + \underline{\hspace{1cm}} = 11$

7) $5 + \underline{\hspace{1cm}} = 11$

8) $5 + \underline{\hspace{1cm}} = 14$

9) $7 + \underline{\hspace{1cm}} = 10$

10) $5 + \underline{\hspace{1cm}} = 9$

11) $7 + \underline{\hspace{1cm}} = 15$

12) $3 + \underline{\hspace{1cm}} = 5$

13) $9 + \underline{\hspace{1cm}} = 10$

14) $8 + \underline{\hspace{1cm}} = 11$

15) $5 + \underline{\hspace{1cm}} = 13$

16) $6 + \underline{\hspace{1cm}} = 8$

17) $9 + \underline{\hspace{1cm}} = 15$

18) $3 + \underline{\hspace{1cm}} = 9$

19) $2 + \underline{\hspace{1cm}} = 6$

20) $7 + \underline{\hspace{1cm}} = 14$

Find the Missing Addends

Fill in the blanks.

1) $8 + \underline{} = 15$

2) $2 + \underline{} = 3$

3) $8 + \underline{} = 13$

4) $8 + \underline{} = 14$

5) $7 + \underline{} = 11$

6) $4 + \underline{} = 10$

7) $4 + \underline{} = 7$

8) $6 + \underline{} = 13$

9) $3 + \underline{} = 6$

10) $9 + \underline{} = 13$

11) $4 + \underline{} = 13$

12) $3 + \underline{} = 9$

13) $6 + \underline{} = 9$

14) $1 + \underline{} = 7$

15) $9 + \underline{} = 12$

16) $9 + \underline{} = 15$

17) $6 + \underline{} = 15$

18) $3 + \underline{} = 12$

19) $7 + \underline{} = 9$

20) $5 + \underline{} = 6$

Find the Missing Addends

Fill in the blanks.

1) $4 + \underline{} = 10$

2) $5 + \underline{} = 14$

3) $6 + \underline{} = 11$

4) $7 + \underline{} = 15$

5) $3 + \underline{} = 4$

6) $3 + \underline{} = 11$

7) $8 + \underline{} = 12$

8) $8 + \underline{} = 15$

9) $6 + \underline{} = 7$

10) $2 + \underline{} = 7$

11) $4 + \underline{} = 13$

12) $2 + \underline{} = 6$

13) $9 + \underline{} = 10$

14) $5 + \underline{} = 10$

15) $2 + \underline{} = 5$

16) $2 + \underline{} = 3$

17) $9 + \underline{} = 14$

18) $1 + \underline{} = 3$

19) $4 + \underline{} = 11$

20) $6 + \underline{} = 8$

Find the Missing Addends

Fill in the blanks.

1) $4 + \underline{\hphantom{00}} = 13$

2) $3 + \underline{\hphantom{00}} = 12$

3) $8 + \underline{\hphantom{00}} = 9$

4) $9 + \underline{\hphantom{00}} = 17$

5) $7 + \underline{\hphantom{00}} = 16$

6) $8 + \underline{\hphantom{00}} = 12$

7) $1 + \underline{\hphantom{00}} = 10$

8) $8 + \underline{\hphantom{00}} = 11$

9) $8 + \underline{\hphantom{00}} = 15$

10) $8 + \underline{\hphantom{00}} = 17$

11) $6 + \underline{\hphantom{00}} = 8$

12) $7 + \underline{\hphantom{00}} = 15$

13) $1 + \underline{\hphantom{00}} = 8$

14) $1 + \underline{\hphantom{00}} = 9$

15) $5 + \underline{\hphantom{00}} = 6$

16) $3 + \underline{\hphantom{00}} = 11$

17) $5 + \underline{\hphantom{00}} = 7$

18) $4 + \underline{\hphantom{00}} = 12$

19) $2 + \underline{\hphantom{00}} = 11$

20) $9 + \underline{\hphantom{00}} = 10$

SECTION

14

FIND THE MISSING ADDENDS
10's

11 worksheets
20 problems per sheet

Name _____   Date _____

Find the Missing Addends

Fill in the blanks.

1) $70 + \underline{\hspace{1cm}} = 110$

2) $10 + \underline{\hspace{1cm}} = 100$

3) $80 + \underline{\hspace{1cm}} = 140$

4) $20 + \underline{\hspace{1cm}} = 80$

5) $70 + \underline{\hspace{1cm}} = 120$

6) $20 + \underline{\hspace{1cm}} = 90$

7) $50 + \underline{\hspace{1cm}} = 110$

8) $60 + \underline{\hspace{1cm}} = 150$

9) $80 + \underline{\hspace{1cm}} = 100$

10) $20 + \underline{\hspace{1cm}} = 70$

11) $70 + \underline{\hspace{1cm}} = 150$

12) $10 + \underline{\hspace{1cm}} = 90$

13) $10 + \underline{\hspace{1cm}} = 60$

14) $40 + \underline{\hspace{1cm}} = 60$

15) $30 + \underline{\hspace{1cm}} = 60$

16) $10 + \underline{\hspace{1cm}} = 70$

17) $40 + \underline{\hspace{1cm}} = 130$

18) $30 + \underline{\hspace{1cm}} = 100$

19) $30 + \underline{\hspace{1cm}} = 120$

20) $60 + \underline{\hspace{1cm}} = 110$

Find the Missing Addends

Fill in the blanks.

1) $60 + \underline{\quad} = 130$

2) $50 + \underline{\quad} = 70$

3) $10 + \underline{\quad} = 50$

4) $70 + \underline{\quad} = 140$

5) $50 + \underline{\quad} = 110$

6) $70 + \underline{\quad} = 90$

7) $50 + \underline{\quad} = 60$

8) $20 + \underline{\quad} = 60$

9) $90 + \underline{\quad} = 120$

10) $60 + \underline{\quad} = 140$

11) $10 + \underline{\quad} = 70$

12) $30 + \underline{\quad} = 70$

13) $90 + \underline{\quad} = 100$

14) $30 + \underline{\quad} = 60$

15) $80 + \underline{\quad} = 130$

16) $10 + \underline{\quad} = 60$

17) $60 + \underline{\quad} = 120$

18) $80 + \underline{\quad} = 140$

19) $80 + \underline{\quad} = 160$

20) $30 + \underline{\quad} = 110$

Find the Missing Addends

Fill in the blanks.

1) $70 + \rule{1cm}{0.4pt} = 80$

2) $80 + \rule{1cm}{0.4pt} = 100$

3) $30 + \rule{1cm}{0.4pt} = 70$

4) $10 + \rule{1cm}{0.4pt} = 50$

5) $20 + \rule{1cm}{0.4pt} = 110$

6) $50 + \rule{1cm}{0.4pt} = 70$

7) $80 + \rule{1cm}{0.4pt} = 160$

8) $60 + \rule{1cm}{0.4pt} = 100$

9) $80 + \rule{1cm}{0.4pt} = 140$

10) $80 + \rule{1cm}{0.4pt} = 120$

11) $40 + \rule{1cm}{0.4pt} = 80$

12) $10 + \rule{1cm}{0.4pt} = 20$

13) $70 + \rule{1cm}{0.4pt} = 90$

14) $50 + \rule{1cm}{0.4pt} = 100$

15) $90 + \rule{1cm}{0.4pt} = 130$

16) $80 + \rule{1cm}{0.4pt} = 170$

17) $40 + \rule{1cm}{0.4pt} = 100$

18) $90 + \rule{1cm}{0.4pt} = 160$

19) $60 + \rule{1cm}{0.4pt} = 150$

20) $70 + \rule{1cm}{0.4pt} = 120$

Find the Missing Addends

Fill in the blanks.

1) $20 + \underline{\hspace{1.5cm}} = 90$

2) $60 + \underline{\hspace{1.5cm}} = 130$

3) $30 + \underline{\hspace{1.5cm}} = 50$

4) $40 + \underline{\hspace{1.5cm}} = 90$

5) $90 + \underline{\hspace{1.5cm}} = 140$

6) $20 + \underline{\hspace{1.5cm}} = 100$

7) $10 + \underline{\hspace{1.5cm}} = 60$

8) $70 + \underline{\hspace{1.5cm}} = 120$

9) $30 + \underline{\hspace{1.5cm}} = 90$

10) $90 + \underline{\hspace{1.5cm}} = 170$

11) $90 + \underline{\hspace{1.5cm}} = 160$

12) $30 + \underline{\hspace{1.5cm}} = 80$

13) $20 + \underline{\hspace{1.5cm}} = 60$

14) $90 + \underline{\hspace{1.5cm}} = 150$

15) $90 + \underline{\hspace{1.5cm}} = 100$

16) $50 + \underline{\hspace{1.5cm}} = 120$

17) $70 + \underline{\hspace{1.5cm}} = 150$

18) $60 + \underline{\hspace{1.5cm}} = 150$

19) $10 + \underline{\hspace{1.5cm}} = 40$

20) $80 + \underline{\hspace{1.5cm}} = 100$

Find the Missing Addends

Fill in the blanks.

1) $80 + \underline{\hphantom{00}} = 90$

2) $60 + \underline{\hphantom{00}} = 110$

3) $60 + \underline{\hphantom{00}} = 90$

4) $20 + \underline{\hphantom{00}} = 50$

5) $50 + \underline{\hphantom{00}} = 60$

6) $10 + \underline{\hphantom{00}} = 70$

7) $90 + \underline{\hphantom{00}} = 150$

8) $80 + \underline{\hphantom{00}} = 160$

9) $80 + \underline{\hphantom{00}} = 130$

10) $50 + \underline{\hphantom{00}} = 80$

11) $30 + \underline{\hphantom{00}} = 100$

12) $60 + \underline{\hphantom{00}} = 120$

13) $70 + \underline{\hphantom{00}} = 90$

14) $20 + \underline{\hphantom{00}} = 30$

15) $40 + \underline{\hphantom{00}} = 60$

16) $10 + \underline{\hphantom{00}} = 50$

17) $40 + \underline{\hphantom{00}} = 80$

18) $90 + \underline{\hphantom{00}} = 180$

19) $80 + \underline{\hphantom{00}} = 150$

20) $20 + \underline{\hphantom{00}} = 70$

Find the Missing Addends

Fill in the blanks.

1) $90 + \_\_\_ = 140$

2) $60 + \_\_\_ = 140$

3) $80 + \_\_\_ = 130$

4) $10 + \_\_\_ = 30$

5) $40 + \_\_\_ = 50$

6) $50 + \_\_\_ = 60$

7) $40 + \_\_\_ = 60$

8) $70 + \_\_\_ = 90$

9) $60 + \_\_\_ = 100$

10) $50 + \_\_\_ = 100$

11) $90 + \_\_\_ = 180$

12) $40 + \_\_\_ = 120$

13) $30 + \_\_\_ = 110$

14) $20 + \_\_\_ = 80$

15) $80 + \_\_\_ = 90$

16) $50 + \_\_\_ = 110$

17) $20 + \_\_\_ = 60$

18) $10 + \_\_\_ = 80$

19) $10 + \_\_\_ = 60$

20) $60 + \_\_\_ = 110$

Find the Missing Addends

Fill in the blanks.

1) $60 + \underline{\quad} = 120$

2) $50 + \underline{\quad} = 100$

3) $30 + \underline{\quad} = 70$

4) $60 + \underline{\quad} = 70$

5) $40 + \underline{\quad} = 110$

6) $40 + \underline{\quad} = 50$

7) $60 + \underline{\quad} = 80$

8) $70 + \underline{\quad} = 160$

9) $70 + \underline{\quad} = 130$

10) $90 + \underline{\quad} = 180$

11) $40 + \underline{\quad} = 80$

12) $70 + \underline{\quad} = 140$

13) $70 + \underline{\quad} = 120$

14) $40 + \underline{\quad} = 70$

15) $80 + \underline{\quad} = 160$

16) $30 + \underline{\quad} = 100$

17) $60 + \underline{\quad} = 150$

18) $20 + \underline{\quad} = 110$

19) $50 + \underline{\quad} = 110$

20) $90 + \underline{\quad} = 100$

Find the Missing Addends

Fill in the blanks.

1) $70 + \underline{\hspace{2cm}} = 140$

2) $90 + \underline{\hspace{2cm}} = 110$

3) $90 + \underline{\hspace{2cm}} = 160$

4) $60 + \underline{\hspace{2cm}} = 90$

5) $20 + \underline{\hspace{2cm}} = 60$

6) $50 + \underline{\hspace{2cm}} = 60$

7) $10 + \underline{\hspace{2cm}} = 70$

8) $50 + \underline{\hspace{2cm}} = 70$

9) $40 + \underline{\hspace{2cm}} = 50$

10) $80 + \underline{\hspace{2cm}} = 110$

11) $70 + \underline{\hspace{2cm}} = 90$

12) $40 + \underline{\hspace{2cm}} = 110$

13) $10 + \underline{\hspace{2cm}} = 90$

14) $40 + \underline{\hspace{2cm}} = 80$

15) $30 + \underline{\hspace{2cm}} = 80$

16) $50 + \underline{\hspace{2cm}} = 130$

17) $20 + \underline{\hspace{2cm}} = 90$

18) $70 + \underline{\hspace{2cm}} = 150$

19) $50 + \underline{\hspace{2cm}} = 100$

20) $90 + \underline{\hspace{2cm}} = 140$

Find the Missing Addends

Fill in the blanks.

1) 80 + ___ = 120

2) 30 + ___ = 90

3) 20 + ___ = 40

4) 20 + ___ = 100

5) 20 + ___ = 90

6) 90 + ___ = 150

7) 50 + ___ = 110

8) 30 + ___ = 50

9) 50 + ___ = 100

10) 50 + ___ = 130

11) 80 + ___ = 130

12) 50 + ___ = 120

13) 60 + ___ = 80

14) 70 + ___ = 110

15) 50 + ___ = 80

16) 40 + ___ = 70

17) 30 + ___ = 80

18) 10 + ___ = 80

19) 70 + ___ = 140

20) 80 + ___ = 170

Find the Missing Addends

Fill in the blanks.

1) 50 + ___ = 110

2) 50 + ___ = 70

3) 10 + ___ = 80

4) 70 + ___ = 160

5) 60 + ___ = 100

6) 30 + ___ = 120

7) 10 + ___ = 20

8) 30 + ___ = 60

9) 80 + ___ = 140

10) 20 + ___ = 40

11) 80 + ___ = 110

12) 80 + ___ = 120

13) 40 + ___ = 80

14) 60 + ___ = 70

15) 40 + ___ = 120

16) 20 + ___ = 50

17) 30 + ___ = 80

18) 40 + ___ = 100

19) 10 + ___ = 40

20) 50 + ___ = 120

Find the Missing Addends

Fill in the blanks.

1) $70 + \underline{\quad} = 150$

2) $30 + \underline{\quad} = 110$

3) $10 + \underline{\quad} = 90$

4) $70 + \underline{\quad} = 160$

5) $10 + \underline{\quad} = 60$

6) $10 + \underline{\quad} = 30$

7) $80 + \underline{\quad} = 110$

8) $90 + \underline{\quad} = 130$

9) $50 + \underline{\quad} = 140$

10) $20 + \underline{\quad} = 70$

11) $20 + \underline{\quad} = 90$

12) $10 + \underline{\quad} = 20$

13) $40 + \underline{\quad} = 120$

14) $70 + \underline{\quad} = 90$

15) $90 + \underline{\quad} = 180$

16) $70 + \underline{\quad} = 120$

17) $80 + \underline{\quad} = 170$

18) $60 + \underline{\quad} = 120$

19) $90 + \underline{\quad} = 140$

20) $30 + \underline{\quad} = 50$

SECTION

15

FIND
THE MISSING
ADDENDS
NO REGROUPING

11 worksheets
20 problems per sheet

Find the Missing Addends

Fill in the blanks.

1) $83 + \underline{\quad} = 89$

2) $\underline{\quad} + 2 = 59$

3) $67 + \underline{\quad} = 68$

4) $\underline{\quad} + 6 = 28$

5) $51 + \underline{\quad} = 54$

6) $\underline{\quad} + 2 = 65$

7) $12 + \underline{\quad} = 16$

8) $\underline{\quad} + 8 = 79$

9) $16 + \underline{\quad} = 18$

10) $\underline{\quad} + 4 = 68$

11) $\underline{\quad} + 6 = 76$

12) $54 + \underline{\quad} = 56$

13) $\underline{\quad} + 1 = 79$

14) $29 + \underline{\quad} = 30$

15) $\underline{\quad} + 4 = 18$

16) $98 + \underline{\quad} = 99$

17) $\underline{\quad} + 3 = 35$

18) $60 + \underline{\quad} = 64$

19) $\underline{\quad} + 1 = 19$

20) $92 + \underline{\quad} = 95$

Find the Missing Addends

Fill in the blanks.

1) $95 + \underline{} = 96$

2) $\underline{} + 1 = 59$

3) $36 + \underline{} = 39$

4) $\underline{} + 1 = 50$

5) $72 + \underline{} = 75$

6) $\underline{} + 3 = 37$

7) $90 + \underline{} = 95$

8) $\underline{} + 7 = 48$

9) $86 + \underline{} = 89$

10) $\underline{} + 7 = 18$

11) $\underline{} + 3 = 69$

12) $93 + \underline{} = 94$

13) $\underline{} + 1 = 18$

14) $12 + \underline{} = 17$

15) $\underline{} + 4 = 37$

16) $76 + \underline{} = 78$

17) $\underline{} + 5 = 58$

18) $68 + \underline{} = 69$

19) $\underline{} + 1 = 75$

20) $23 + \underline{} = 28$

Find the Missing Addends

Fill in the blanks.

1) $51 + \underline{} = 59$

2) $\underline{} + 3 = 29$

3) $21 + \underline{} = 24$

4) $\underline{} + 2 = 59$

5) $15 + \underline{} = 16$

6) $\underline{} + 2 = 49$

7) $96 + \underline{} = 98$

8) $\underline{} + 1 = 79$

9) $34 + \underline{} = 38$

10) $\underline{} + 1 = 57$

11) $\underline{} + 2 = 13$

12) $85 + \underline{} = 89$

13) $\underline{} + 1 = 19$

14) $72 + \underline{} = 79$

15) $\underline{} + 1 = 23$

16) $20 + \underline{} = 27$

17) $\underline{} + 2 = 57$

18) $94 + \underline{} = 95$

19) $\underline{} + 1 = 68$

20) $90 + \underline{} = 98$

Find the Missing Addends

Fill in the blanks.

1) $46 + \underline{} = 49$

2) $\underline{} + 3 = 28$

3) $70 + \underline{} = 78$

4) $\underline{} + 2 = 83$

5) $42 + \underline{} = 43$

6) $\underline{} + 1 = 30$

7) $53 + \underline{} = 58$

8) $\underline{} + 3 = 29$

9) $62 + \underline{} = 63$

10) $\underline{} + 1 = 96$

11) $\underline{} + 3 = 37$

12) $66 + \underline{} = 69$

13) $\underline{} + 1 = 59$

14) $39 + \underline{} = 40$

15) $\underline{} + 1 = 90$

16) $17 + \underline{} = 19$

17) $\underline{} + 1 = 38$

18) $69 + \underline{} = 70$

19) $\underline{} + 3 = 58$

20) $67 + \underline{} = 69$

Find the Missing Addends

Fill in the blanks.

1) $36 + \rule{1cm}{0.15mm} = 38$

2) $\rule{1cm}{0.15mm} + 7 = 67$

3) $31 + \rule{1cm}{0.15mm} = 33$

4) $\rule{1cm}{0.15mm} + 1 = 35$

5) $20 + \rule{1cm}{0.15mm} = 29$

6) $\rule{1cm}{0.15mm} + 6 = 98$

7) $33 + \rule{1cm}{0.15mm} = 38$

8) $\rule{1cm}{0.15mm} + 2 = 68$

9) $23 + \rule{1cm}{0.15mm} = 28$

10) $\rule{1cm}{0.15mm} + 5 = 85$

11) $\rule{1cm}{0.15mm} + 1 = 38$

12) $26 + \rule{1cm}{0.15mm} = 29$

13) $\rule{1cm}{0.15mm} + 2 = 58$

14) $83 + \rule{1cm}{0.15mm} = 85$

15) $\rule{1cm}{0.15mm} + 7 = 59$

16) $87 + \rule{1cm}{0.15mm} = 89$

17) $\rule{1cm}{0.15mm} + 1 = 20$

18) $14 + \rule{1cm}{0.15mm} = 17$

19) $\rule{1cm}{0.15mm} + 6 = 99$

20) $35 + \rule{1cm}{0.15mm} = 38$

Find the Missing Addends

Fill in the blanks.

1) $41 + \underline{\quad} = 44$

2) $\underline{\quad} + 2 = 29$

3) $23 + \underline{\quad} = 29$

4) $\underline{\quad} + 1 = 61$

5) $35 + \underline{\quad} = 36$

6) $\underline{\quad} + 1 = 69$

7) $55 + \underline{\quad} = 58$

8) $\underline{\quad} + 3 = 79$

9) $94 + \underline{\quad} = 97$

10) $\underline{\quad} + 1 = 29$

11) $\underline{\quad} + 3 = 16$

12) $36 + \underline{\quad} = 37$

13) $\underline{\quad} + 1 = 70$

14) $29 + \underline{\quad} = 30$

15) $\underline{\quad} + 1 = 60$

16) $79 + \underline{\quad} = 80$

17) $\underline{\quad} + 4 = 56$

18) $40 + \underline{\quad} = 42$

19) $\underline{\quad} + 2 = 88$

20) $45 + \underline{\quad} = 46$

Find the Missing Addends

Fill in the blanks.

1) $67 + \underline{\hspace{1cm}} = 68$

2) $\underline{\hspace{1cm}} + 2 = 73$

3) $81 + \underline{\hspace{1cm}} = 86$

4) $\underline{\hspace{1cm}} + 9 = 69$

5) $18 + \underline{\hspace{1cm}} = 19$

6) $\underline{\hspace{1cm}} + 3 = 99$

7) $36 + \underline{\hspace{1cm}} = 39$

8) $\underline{\hspace{1cm}} + 1 = 39$

9) $89 + \underline{\hspace{1cm}} = 90$

10) $\underline{\hspace{1cm}} + 4 = 24$

11) $\underline{\hspace{1cm}} + 3 = 44$

12) $22 + \underline{\hspace{1cm}} = 25$

13) $\underline{\hspace{1cm}} + 1 = 20$

14) $61 + \underline{\hspace{1cm}} = 63$

15) $\underline{\hspace{1cm}} + 1 = 49$

16) $97 + \underline{\hspace{1cm}} = 99$

17) $\underline{\hspace{1cm}} + 1 = 50$

18) $83 + \underline{\hspace{1cm}} = 84$

19) $\underline{\hspace{1cm}} + 6 = 56$

20) $28 + \underline{\hspace{1cm}} = 29$

Find the Missing Addends

Fill in the blanks.

1) $51 + \underline{} = 58$

2) $\underline{} + 3 = 49$

3) $90 + \underline{} = 98$

4) $\underline{} + 1 = 50$

5) $96 + \underline{} = 97$

6) $\underline{} + 1 = 96$

7) $44 + \underline{} = 46$

8) $\underline{} + 2 = 76$

9) $92 + \underline{} = 96$

10) $\underline{} + 3 = 87$

11) $\underline{} + 1 = 90$

12) $72 + \underline{} = 77$

13) $\underline{} + 2 = 45$

14) $21 + \underline{} = 22$

15) $\underline{} + 6 = 76$

16) $30 + \underline{} = 37$

17) $\underline{} + 2 = 58$

18) $78 + \underline{} = 79$

19) $\underline{} + 3 = 76$

20) $23 + \underline{} = 25$

Find the Missing Addends

Fill in the blanks.

1) $15 + \underline{\quad} = 19$

2) $\underline{\quad} + 2 = 32$

3) $92 + \underline{\quad} = 99$

4) $\underline{\quad} + 3 = 36$

5) $82 + \underline{\quad} = 86$

6) $\underline{\quad} + 2 = 73$

7) $52 + \underline{\quad} = 55$

8) $\underline{\quad} + 1 = 35$

9) $69 + \underline{\quad} = 70$

10) $\underline{\quad} + 3 = 79$

11) $\underline{\quad} + 8 = 89$

12) $55 + \underline{\quad} = 57$

13) $\underline{\quad} + 6 = 69$

14) $94 + \underline{\quad} = 98$

15) $\underline{\quad} + 1 = 88$

16) $29 + \underline{\quad} = 30$

17) $\underline{\quad} + 4 = 44$

18) $17 + \underline{\quad} = 19$

19) $\underline{\quad} + 1 = 80$

20) $66 + \underline{\quad} = 67$

Find the Missing Addends

Fill in the blanks.

1) $11 + \_\_\_ = 19$

2) $\_\_\_ + 1 = 59$

3) $37 + \_\_\_ = 39$

4) $\_\_\_ + 5 = 75$

5) $40 + \_\_\_ = 43$

6) $\_\_\_ + 5 = 48$

7) $20 + \_\_\_ = 27$

8) $\_\_\_ + 2 = 49$

9) $64 + \_\_\_ = 67$

10) $\_\_\_ + 1 = 80$

11) $\_\_\_ + 4 = 89$

12) $98 + \_\_\_ = 99$

13) $\_\_\_ + 2 = 48$

14) $87 + \_\_\_ = 89$

15) $\_\_\_ + 2 = 19$

16) $67 + \_\_\_ = 69$

17) $\_\_\_ + 1 = 69$

18) $72 + \_\_\_ = 79$

19) $\_\_\_ + 3 = 58$

20) $60 + \_\_\_ = 67$

Find the Missing Addends

Fill in the blanks.

1) $54 + \_\_\_ = 58$

2) $\_\_\_ + 2 = 67$

3) $33 + \_\_\_ = 34$

4) $\_\_\_ + 1 = 99$

5) $92 + \_\_\_ = 95$

6) $\_\_\_ + 2 = 69$

7) $31 + \_\_\_ = 34$

8) $\_\_\_ + 1 = 39$

9) $95 + \_\_\_ = 99$

10) $\_\_\_ + 2 = 79$

11) $\_\_\_ + 3 = 58$

12) $74 + \_\_\_ = 79$

13) $\_\_\_ + 5 = 19$

14) $85 + \_\_\_ = 89$

15) $\_\_\_ + 5 = 98$

16) $70 + \_\_\_ = 73$

17) $\_\_\_ + 1 = 91$

18) $96 + \_\_\_ = 99$

19) $\_\_\_ + 4 = 77$

20) $52 + \_\_\_ = 56$

SECTION

FIND
THE MISSING
SUBTRAHENDS
SUBTRACTION FACTS

11 worksheets
20 problems per sheet

Find the Missing Subtrahends

Fill in the blanks.

1) $5 - \underline{} = 3$

2) $10 - \underline{} = 7$

3) $2 - \underline{} = 0$

4) $10 - \underline{} = 9$

5) $15 - \underline{} = 6$

6) $13 - \underline{} = 9$

7) $7 - \underline{} = 1$

8) $8 - \underline{} = 6$

9) $4 - \underline{} = 0$

10) $8 - \underline{} = 7$

11) $17 - \underline{} = 9$

12) $18 - \underline{} = 9$

13) $11 - \underline{} = 5$

14) $16 - \underline{} = 9$

15) $3 - \underline{} = 2$

16) $16 - \underline{} = 8$

17) $4 - \underline{} = 2$

18) $15 - \underline{} = 7$

19) $6 - \underline{} = 1$

20) $7 - \underline{} = 3$

Find the Missing Subtrahends

Fill in the blanks.

1) $2 - \underline{} = 0$

2) $8 - \underline{} = 2$

3) $15 - \underline{} = 6$

4) $10 - \underline{} = 1$

5) $16 - \underline{} = 9$

6) $3 - \underline{} = 1$

7) $11 - \underline{} = 5$

8) $4 - \underline{} = 3$

9) $6 - \underline{} = 2$

10) $7 - \underline{} = 6$

11) $6 - \underline{} = 1$

12) $4 - \underline{} = 2$

13) $14 - \underline{} = 8$

14) $17 - \underline{} = 9$

15) $18 - \underline{} = 9$

16) $11 - \underline{} = 9$

17) $6 - \underline{} = 3$

18) $13 - \underline{} = 9$

19) $14 - \underline{} = 5$

20) $12 - \underline{} = 8$

Find the Missing Subtrahends

Fill in the blanks.

1) $18 - \underline{} = 9$

2) $4 - \underline{} = 3$

3) $8 - \underline{} = 1$

4) $8 - \underline{} = 6$

5) $5 - \underline{} = 2$

6) $10 - \underline{} = 5$

7) $10 - \underline{} = 8$

8) $13 - \underline{} = 8$

9) $6 - \underline{} = 2$

10) $2 - \underline{} = 0$

11) $15 - \underline{} = 7$

12) $11 - \underline{} = 4$

13) $9 - \underline{} = 1$

14) $14 - \underline{} = 7$

15) $2 - \underline{} = 1$

16) $14 - \underline{} = 5$

17) $14 - \underline{} = 6$

18) $6 - \underline{} = 4$

19) $11 - \underline{} = 6$

20) $13 - \underline{} = 9$

Find the Missing Subtrahends

Fill in the blanks.

1) $14 - \underline{\hphantom{00}} = 7$

2) $3 - \underline{\hphantom{00}} = 0$

3) $7 - \underline{\hphantom{00}} = 0$

4) $17 - \underline{\hphantom{00}} = 8$

5) $13 - \underline{\hphantom{00}} = 5$

6) $15 - \underline{\hphantom{00}} = 6$

7) $2 - \underline{\hphantom{00}} = 1$

8) $6 - \underline{\hphantom{00}} = 2$

9) $12 - \underline{\hphantom{00}} = 4$

10) $14 - \underline{\hphantom{00}} = 8$

11) $15 - \underline{\hphantom{00}} = 8$

12) $3 - \underline{\hphantom{00}} = 2$

13) $9 - \underline{\hphantom{00}} = 7$

14) $16 - \underline{\hphantom{00}} = 8$

15) $18 - \underline{\hphantom{00}} = 9$

16) $13 - \underline{\hphantom{00}} = 8$

17) $12 - \underline{\hphantom{00}} = 8$

18) $7 - \underline{\hphantom{00}} = 6$

19) $11 - \underline{\hphantom{00}} = 3$

20) $8 - \underline{\hphantom{00}} = 5$

Find the Missing Subtrahends

Fill in the blanks.

1) $18 - \underline{} = 9$

2) $7 - \underline{} = 0$

3) $17 - \underline{} = 8$

4) $6 - \underline{} = 3$

5) $9 - \underline{} = 8$

6) $4 - \underline{} = 2$

7) $9 - \underline{} = 2$

8) $16 - \underline{} = 7$

9) $11 - \underline{} = 5$

10) $3 - \underline{} = 2$

11) $7 - \underline{} = 4$

12) $14 - \underline{} = 7$

13) $9 - \underline{} = 4$

14) $16 - \underline{} = 9$

15) $13 - \underline{} = 9$

16) $8 - \underline{} = 0$

17) $14 - \underline{} = 6$

18) $4 - \underline{} = 0$

19) $8 - \underline{} = 5$

20) $16 - \underline{} = 8$

Find the Missing Subtrahends

Fill in the blanks.

1) $11 - \underline{} = 7$

2) $11 - \underline{} = 8$

3) $5 - \underline{} = 1$

4) $3 - \underline{} = 0$

5) $7 - \underline{} = 2$

6) $6 - \underline{} = 4$

7) $15 - \underline{} = 9$

8) $11 - \underline{} = 4$

9) $6 - \underline{} = 1$

10) $7 - \underline{} = 1$

11) $8 - \underline{} = 4$

12) $6 - \underline{} = 2$

13) $9 - \underline{} = 0$

14) $4 - \underline{} = 0$

15) $8 - \underline{} = 1$

16) $9 - \underline{} = 2$

17) $7 - \underline{} = 4$

18) $12 - \underline{} = 8$

19) $8 - \underline{} = 6$

20) $10 - \underline{} = 5$

Find the Missing Subtrahends

Fill in the blanks.

1) $6 - \underline{} = 3$

2) $16 - \underline{} = 8$

3) $17 - \underline{} = 8$

4) $14 - \underline{} = 9$

5) $7 - \underline{} = 4$

6) $10 - \underline{} = 6$

7) $14 - \underline{} = 5$

8) $17 - \underline{} = 9$

9) $12 - \underline{} = 4$

10) $4 - \underline{} = 3$

11) $15 - \underline{} = 7$

12) $13 - \underline{} = 9$

13) $3 - \underline{} = 1$

14) $2 - \underline{} = 0$

15) $4 - \underline{} = 1$

16) $7 - \underline{} = 1$

17) $18 - \underline{} = 9$

18) $13 - \underline{} = 5$

19) $15 - \underline{} = 8$

20) $8 - \underline{} = 6$

Find the Missing Subtrahends

Fill in the blanks.

1) $7 - \underline{} = 6$

2) $12 - \underline{} = 8$

3) $15 - \underline{} = 9$

4) $14 - \underline{} = 7$

5) $14 - \underline{} = 8$

6) $13 - \underline{} = 4$

7) $17 - \underline{} = 9$

8) $13 - \underline{} = 6$

9) $12 - \underline{} = 7$

10) $7 - \underline{} = 1$

11) $7 - \underline{} = 2$

12) $8 - \underline{} = 0$

13) $11 - \underline{} = 6$

14) $9 - \underline{} = 0$

15) $4 - \underline{} = 1$

16) $7 - \underline{} = 5$

17) $5 - \underline{} = 3$

18) $2 - \underline{} = 1$

19) $3 - \underline{} = 2$

20) $16 - \underline{} = 8$

www.claymaze.com

Find the Missing Subtrahends

Fill in the blanks.

1) $9 - \underline{\quad} = 3$

2) $6 - \underline{\quad} = 5$

3) $16 - \underline{\quad} = 8$

4) $14 - \underline{\quad} = 9$

5) $4 - \underline{\quad} = 0$

6) $13 - \underline{\quad} = 8$

7) $13 - \underline{\quad} = 5$

8) $17 - \underline{\quad} = 9$

9) $6 - \underline{\quad} = 4$

10) $11 - \underline{\quad} = 6$

11) $7 - \underline{\quad} = 1$

12) $9 - \underline{\quad} = 2$

13) $12 - \underline{\quad} = 4$

14) $3 - \underline{\quad} = 0$

15) $9 - \underline{\quad} = 5$

16) $16 - \underline{\quad} = 7$

17) $9 - \underline{\quad} = 4$

18) $4 - \underline{\quad} = 2$

19) $17 - \underline{\quad} = 8$

20) $6 - \underline{\quad} = 1$

Find the Missing Subtrahends

Fill in the blanks.

1) $13 - \underline{} = 9$

2) $12 - \underline{} = 8$

3) $6 - \underline{} = 0$

4) $3 - \underline{} = 1$

5) $17 - \underline{} = 9$

6) $3 - \underline{} = 2$

7) $9 - \underline{} = 4$

8) $6 - \underline{} = 1$

9) $10 - \underline{} = 3$

10) $9 - \underline{} = 8$

11) $10 - \underline{} = 5$

12) $6 - \underline{} = 4$

13) $7 - \underline{} = 6$

14) $15 - \underline{} = 7$

15) $5 - \underline{} = 3$

16) $13 - \underline{} = 7$

17) $16 - \underline{} = 7$

18) $14 - \underline{} = 7$

19) $18 - \underline{} = 9$

20) $17 - \underline{} = 8$

Find the Missing Subtrahends

Fill in the blanks.

1) $17 - \underline{\quad} = 9$

2) $11 - \underline{\quad} = 3$

3) $12 - \underline{\quad} = 5$

4) $14 - \underline{\quad} = 6$

5) $9 - \underline{\quad} = 2$

6) $7 - \underline{\quad} = 4$

7) $4 - \underline{\quad} = 1$

8) $10 - \underline{\quad} = 9$

9) $15 - \underline{\quad} = 7$

10) $16 - \underline{\quad} = 7$

11) $4 - \underline{\quad} = 3$

12) $18 - \underline{\quad} = 9$

13) $13 - \underline{\quad} = 5$

14) $7 - \underline{\quad} = 1$

15) $12 - \underline{\quad} = 4$

16) $9 - \underline{\quad} = 0$

17) $8 - \underline{\quad} = 7$

18) $7 - \underline{\quad} = 6$

19) $16 - \underline{\quad} = 8$

20) $12 - \underline{\quad} = 8$

www.claymaze.com

SECTION

FIND
THE MISSING
SUBTRAHENDS
10's

11 worksheets
20 problems per sheet

Find the Missing Subtrahends

Fill in the blanks.

1) $130 - \underline{} = 50$

2) $90 - \underline{} = 80$

3) $110 - \underline{} = 30$

4) $60 - \underline{} = 10$

5) $50 - \underline{} = 30$

6) $80 - \underline{} = 40$

7) $150 - \underline{} = 80$

8) $90 - \underline{} = 60$

9) $60 - \underline{} = 20$

10) $170 - \underline{} = 80$

11) $90 - \underline{} = 60$

12) $140 - \underline{} = 50$

13) $120 - \underline{} = 50$

14) $160 - \underline{} = 80$

15) $110 - \underline{} = 70$

16) $70 - \underline{} = 40$

17) $180 - \underline{} = 90$

18) $170 - \underline{} = 90$

19) $150 - \underline{} = 80$

20) $50 - \underline{} = 30$

Find the Missing Subtrahends

Fill in the blanks.

1) $150 - \underline{} = 90$

2) $70 - \underline{} = 20$

3) $130 - \underline{} = 40$

4) $90 - \underline{} = 20$

5) $90 - \underline{} = 60$

6) $80 - \underline{} = 20$

7) $160 - \underline{} = 70$

8) $50 - \underline{} = 10$

9) $60 - \underline{} = 10$

10) $150 - \underline{} = 60$

11) $90 - \underline{} = 70$

12) $130 - \underline{} = 80$

13) $140 - \underline{} = 50$

14) $100 - \underline{} = 20$

15) $130 - \underline{} = 50$

16) $80 - \underline{} = 70$

17) $130 - \underline{} = 60$

18) $150 - \underline{} = 70$

19) $110 - \underline{} = 30$

20) $90 - \underline{} = 30$

Name _____ Date _____

Find the Missing Subtrahends

Fill in the blanks.

1) $110 - \underline{\hphantom{00}} = 60$

2) $50 - \underline{\hphantom{00}} = 10$

3) $100 - \underline{\hphantom{00}} = 60$

4) $70 - \underline{\hphantom{00}} = 20$

5) $120 - \underline{\hphantom{00}} = 50$

6) $70 - \underline{\hphantom{00}} = 30$

7) $120 - \underline{\hphantom{00}} = 40$

8) $50 - \underline{\hphantom{00}} = 20$

9) $80 - \underline{\hphantom{00}} = 10$

10) $90 - \underline{\hphantom{00}} = 10$

11) $150 - \underline{\hphantom{00}} = 90$

12) $110 - \underline{\hphantom{00}} = 20$

13) $130 - \underline{\hphantom{00}} = 40$

14) $80 - \underline{\hphantom{00}} = 20$

15) $90 - \underline{\hphantom{00}} = 70$

16) $30 - \underline{\hphantom{00}} = 20$

17) $70 - \underline{\hphantom{00}} = 50$

18) $130 - \underline{\hphantom{00}} = 80$

19) $100 - \underline{\hphantom{00}} = 90$

20) $20 - \underline{\hphantom{00}} = 10$

www.claymaze.com

Find the Missing Subtrahends

Fill in the blanks.

1) $140 - \underline{\quad} = 60$

2) $130 - \underline{\quad} = 60$

3) $110 - \underline{\quad} = 90$

4) $100 - \underline{\quad} = 40$

5) $140 - \underline{\quad} = 70$

6) $170 - \underline{\quad} = 80$

7) $40 - \underline{\quad} = 30$

8) $80 - \underline{\quad} = 10$

9) $110 - \underline{\quad} = 80$

10) $50 - \underline{\quad} = 40$

11) $20 - \underline{\quad} = 10$

12) $160 - \underline{\quad} = 70$

13) $60 - \underline{\quad} = 50$

14) $60 - \underline{\quad} = 10$

15) $160 - \underline{\quad} = 80$

16) $90 - \underline{\quad} = 80$

17) $80 - \underline{\quad} = 30$

18) $90 - \underline{\quad} = 40$

19) $170 - \underline{\quad} = 90$

20) $100 - \underline{\quad} = 70$

Find the Missing Subtrahends

Fill in the blanks.

1) $100 - \underline{\hspace{1cm}} = 60$

2) $20 - \underline{\hspace{1cm}} = 10$

3) $110 - \underline{\hspace{1cm}} = 90$

4) $140 - \underline{\hspace{1cm}} = 80$

5) $110 - \underline{\hspace{1cm}} = 70$

6) $90 - \underline{\hspace{1cm}} = 10$

7) $40 - \underline{\hspace{1cm}} = 30$

8) $70 - \underline{\hspace{1cm}} = 20$

9) $80 - \underline{\hspace{1cm}} = 50$

10) $150 - \underline{\hspace{1cm}} = 80$

11) $50 - \underline{\hspace{1cm}} = 40$

12) $110 - \underline{\hspace{1cm}} = 20$

13) $160 - \underline{\hspace{1cm}} = 90$

14) $100 - \underline{\hspace{1cm}} = 10$

15) $70 - \underline{\hspace{1cm}} = 30$

16) $140 - \underline{\hspace{1cm}} = 60$

17) $60 - \underline{\hspace{1cm}} = 30$

18) $70 - \underline{\hspace{1cm}} = 50$

19) $70 - \underline{\hspace{1cm}} = 60$

20) $170 - \underline{\hspace{1cm}} = 90$

www.claymaze.com

Find the Missing Subtrahends

Fill in the blanks.

1) $120 - \underline{\quad} = 90$

2) $140 - \underline{\quad} = 80$

3) $90 - \underline{\quad} = 10$

4) $110 - \underline{\quad} = 80$

5) $120 - \underline{\quad} = 70$

6) $150 - \underline{\quad} = 70$

7) $140 - \underline{\quad} = 60$

8) $110 - \underline{\quad} = 30$

9) $70 - \underline{\quad} = 50$

10) $90 - \underline{\quad} = 40$

11) $30 - \underline{\quad} = 10$

12) $70 - \underline{\quad} = 20$

13) $100 - \underline{\quad} = 50$

14) $100 - \underline{\quad} = 90$

15) $150 - \underline{\quad} = 80$

16) $40 - \underline{\quad} = 10$

17) $40 - \underline{\quad} = 30$

18) $130 - \underline{\quad} = 50$

19) $100 - \underline{\quad} = 30$

20) $40 - \underline{\quad} = 20$

Find the Missing Subtrahends

Fill in the blanks.

1) 40 – ___ = 30

2) 100 – ___ = 90

3) 70 – ___ = 40

4) 150 – ___ = 90

5) 80 – ___ = 10

6) 70 – ___ = 10

7) 100 – ___ = 70

8) 90 – ___ = 50

9) 110 – ___ = 20

10) 40 – ___ = 20

11) 90 – ___ = 40

12) 160 – ___ = 90

13) 110 – ___ = 90

14) 120 – ___ = 40

15) 50 – ___ = 30

16) 120 – ___ = 90

17) 90 – ___ = 30

18) 100 – ___ = 40

19) 90 – ___ = 60

20) 50 – ___ = 20

Find the Missing Subtrahends

Fill in the blanks.

1) $60 - \underline{\hspace{2em}} = 20$

2) $50 - \underline{\hspace{2em}} = 40$

3) $90 - \underline{\hspace{2em}} = 80$

4) $160 - \underline{\hspace{2em}} = 80$

5) $70 - \underline{\hspace{2em}} = 20$

6) $170 - \underline{\hspace{2em}} = 80$

7) $140 - \underline{\hspace{2em}} = 70$

8) $140 - \underline{\hspace{2em}} = 60$

9) $120 - \underline{\hspace{2em}} = 40$

10) $100 - \underline{\hspace{2em}} = 90$

11) $130 - \underline{\hspace{2em}} = 70$

12) $70 - \underline{\hspace{2em}} = 30$

13) $100 - \underline{\hspace{2em}} = 60$

14) $130 - \underline{\hspace{2em}} = 60$

15) $110 - \underline{\hspace{2em}} = 90$

16) $140 - \underline{\hspace{2em}} = 80$

17) $90 - \underline{\hspace{2em}} = 40$

18) $70 - \underline{\hspace{2em}} = 60$

19) $160 - \underline{\hspace{2em}} = 90$

20) $80 - \underline{\hspace{2em}} = 20$

Find the Missing Subtrahends

Fill in the blanks.

1) $110 - \underline{\hspace{1.5em}} = 80$

2) $90 - \underline{\hspace{1.5em}} = 30$

3) $150 - \underline{\hspace{1.5em}} = 80$

4) $70 - \underline{\hspace{1.5em}} = 60$

5) $30 - \underline{\hspace{1.5em}} = 20$

6) $70 - \underline{\hspace{1.5em}} = 50$

7) $130 - \underline{\hspace{1.5em}} = 40$

8) $140 - \underline{\hspace{1.5em}} = 80$

9) $110 - \underline{\hspace{1.5em}} = 90$

10) $140 - \underline{\hspace{1.5em}} = 90$

11) $80 - \underline{\hspace{1.5em}} = 70$

12) $50 - \underline{\hspace{1.5em}} = 40$

13) $60 - \underline{\hspace{1.5em}} = 50$

14) $100 - \underline{\hspace{1.5em}} = 80$

15) $150 - \underline{\hspace{1.5em}} = 90$

16) $100 - \underline{\hspace{1.5em}} = 50$

17) $120 - \underline{\hspace{1.5em}} = 80$

18) $100 - \underline{\hspace{1.5em}} = 90$

19) $80 - \underline{\hspace{1.5em}} = 40$

20) $40 - \underline{\hspace{1.5em}} = 10$

Find the Missing Subtrahends

Fill in the blanks.

1) $70 - \underline{\hspace{1cm}} = 10$

2) $80 - \underline{\hspace{1cm}} = 30$

3) $140 - \underline{\hspace{1cm}} = 80$

4) $160 - \underline{\hspace{1cm}} = 70$

5) $100 - \underline{\hspace{1cm}} = 20$

6) $130 - \underline{\hspace{1cm}} = 90$

7) $70 - \underline{\hspace{1cm}} = 60$

8) $140 - \underline{\hspace{1cm}} = 70$

9) $120 - \underline{\hspace{1cm}} = 30$

10) $60 - \underline{\hspace{1cm}} = 20$

11) $80 - \underline{\hspace{1cm}} = 70$

12) $120 - \underline{\hspace{1cm}} = 90$

13) $120 - \underline{\hspace{1cm}} = 80$

14) $160 - \underline{\hspace{1cm}} = 80$

15) $30 - \underline{\hspace{1cm}} = 20$

16) $120 - \underline{\hspace{1cm}} = 50$

17) $90 - \underline{\hspace{1cm}} = 80$

18) $20 - \underline{\hspace{1cm}} = 10$

19) $90 - \underline{\hspace{1cm}} = 10$

20) $70 - \underline{\hspace{1cm}} = 20$

Find the Missing Subtrahends

Fill in the blanks.

1) $80 - \underline{} = 40$

2) $130 - \underline{} = 60$

3) $130 - \underline{} = 90$

4) $110 - \underline{} = 80$

5) $120 - \underline{} = 60$

6) $150 - \underline{} = 60$

7) $80 - \underline{} = 20$

8) $60 - \underline{} = 30$

9) $70 - \underline{} = 10$

10) $150 - \underline{} = 90$

11) $50 - \underline{} = 30$

12) $100 - \underline{} = 80$

13) $110 - \underline{} = 50$

14) $140 - \underline{} = 60$

15) $110 - \underline{} = 20$

16) $70 - \underline{} = 40$

17) $110 - \underline{} = 70$

18) $120 - \underline{} = 80$

19) $100 - \underline{} = 30$

20) $170 - \underline{} = 80$

www.claymaze.com

SOLUTIONS

SOLUTIONS TO PROBLEMS

Sections 1 - 17

Addition Facts

Add.

1) 1 +5 = 6	2) 6 +2 = 8	3) 2 +9 = 11	4) 4 +2 = 6	5) 7 +4 = 11
6) 1 +3 = 4	7) 5 +2 = 7	8) 2 +4 = 6	9) 8 +2 = 10	10) 7 +2 = 9
11) 3 +6 = 9	12) 1 +6 = 7	13) 2 +5 = 7	14) 1 +1 = 2	15) 6 +8 = 14
16) 3 +2 = 5	17) 6 +7 = 13	18) 7 +9 = 16	19) 7 +7 = 14	20) 9 +9 = 18

Addition Facts

Add.

1) 6 +2 = 8	2) 4 +2 = 6	3) 9 +3 = 12	4) 4 +7 = 11	5) 2 +4 = 6
6) 5 +5 = 10	7) 5 +9 = 14	8) 5 +8 = 13	9) 9 +4 = 13	10) 5 +4 = 9
11) 3 +7 = 10	12) 7 +7 = 14	13) 1 +8 = 9	14) 5 +3 = 8	15) 7 +8 = 15
16) 8 +9 = 17	17) 6 +9 = 15	18) 9 +6 = 15	19) 8 +8 = 16	20) 7 +6 = 13

Addition Facts

Add.

1) 5 +1 = 6	2) 5 +3 = 8	3) 8 +8 = 16	4) 4 +3 = 7	5) 1 +3 = 4
6) 6 +8 = 14	7) 5 +8 = 13	8) 9 +3 = 12	9) 2 +9 = 11	10) 1 +9 = 10
11) 7 +2 = 9	12) 6 +9 = 15	13) 9 +8 = 17	14) 7 +6 = 13	15) 7 +3 = 10
16) 9 +2 = 11	17) 2 +4 = 6	18) 1 +1 = 2	19) 3 +5 = 8	20) 6 +1 = 7

Addition Facts

Add.

1) 3 +7 = 10	2) 3 +1 = 4	3) 2 +1 = 3	4) 5 +8 = 13	5) 8 +4 = 12
6) 2 +5 = 7	7) 4 +7 = 11	8) 2 +6 = 8	9) 1 +9 = 10	10) 4 +2 = 6
11) 3 +9 = 12	12) 8 +1 = 9	13) 8 +3 = 11	14) 8 +2 = 10	15) 5 +5 = 10
16) 1 +7 = 8	17) 6 +8 = 14	18) 9 +7 = 16	19) 7 +5 = 12	20) 3 +5 = 8

Addition Facts

Add.

1) 9 +1 = 10	2) 4 +5 = 9	3) 3 +3 = 6	4) 7 +1 = 8	5) 1 +1 = 2
6) 3 +6 = 9	7) 7 +7 = 14	8) 6 +3 = 9	9) 8 +2 = 10	10) 6 +7 = 13
11) 8 +7 = 15	12) 8 +9 = 17	13) 9 +2 = 11	14) 1 +5 = 6	15) 1 +8 = 9
16) 9 +6 = 15	17) 4 +7 = 11	18) 4 +9 = 13	19) 5 +9 = 14	20) 8 +3 = 11

Addition Facts

Add.

1) 8 +2 = 10	2) 9 +9 = 18	3) 6 +7 = 13	4) 9 +2 = 11	5) 2 +7 = 9
6) 4 +6 = 10	7) 8 +1 = 9	8) 5 +7 = 12	9) 9 +6 = 15	10) 9 +1 = 10
11) 2 +5 = 7	12) 9 +4 = 13	13) 3 +4 = 7	14) 2 +1 = 3	15) 7 +4 = 11
16) 8 +9 = 17	17) 6 +1 = 7	18) 6 +3 = 9	19) 3 +5 = 8	20) 2 +4 = 6

www.claymaze.com

Addition Facts

Add.

1) 6 + 4 = 10
2) 7 + 4 = 11
3) 6 + 6 = 12
4) 5 + 3 = 8
5) 4 + 1 = 5
6) 4 + 9 = 13
7) 8 + 1 = 9
8) 4 + 6 = 10
9) 5 + 9 = 14
10) 2 + 3 = 5
11) 5 + 2 = 7
12) 7 + 2 = 9
13) 7 + 6 = 13
14) 3 + 2 = 5
15) 9 + 4 = 13
16) 2 + 1 = 3
17) 8 + 8 = 16
18) 5 + 8 = 13
19) 7 + 7 = 14
20) 4 + 2 = 6

Addition Facts

Add.

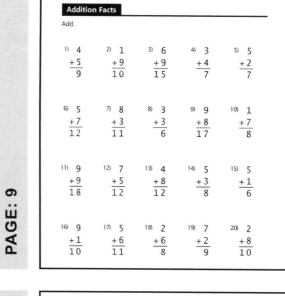

1) 4 + 5 = 9
2) 1 + 9 = 10
3) 6 + 9 = 15
4) 3 + 4 = 7
5) 5 + 2 = 7
6) 5 + 7 = 12
7) 8 + 3 = 11
8) 3 + 3 = 6
9) 9 + 8 = 17
10) 1 + 7 = 8
11) 9 + 9 = 18
12) 7 + 5 = 12
13) 4 + 8 = 12
14) 5 + 3 = 8
15) 5 + 1 = 6
16) 9 + 1 = 10
17) 5 + 6 = 11
18) 2 + 6 = 8
19) 7 + 2 = 9
20) 2 + 8 = 10

Addition Facts

Add.

1) 3 + 8 = 11
2) 1 + 6 = 7
3) 7 + 1 = 8
4) 7 + 6 = 13
5) 5 + 7 = 12
6) 4 + 4 = 8
7) 5 + 8 = 13
8) 7 + 5 = 12
9) 7 + 7 = 14
10) 4 + 2 = 6
11) 3 + 1 = 4
12) 3 + 7 = 10
13) 8 + 3 = 11
14) 9 + 5 = 14
15) 6 + 3 = 9
16) 3 + 9 = 12
17) 5 + 4 = 9
18) 7 + 2 = 9
19) 4 + 9 = 13
20) 4 + 6 = 10

Addition Facts

Add.

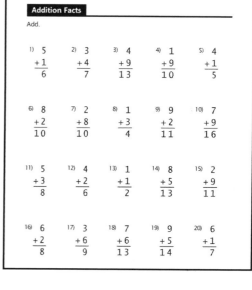

1) 5 + 1 = 6
2) 3 + 4 = 7
3) 4 + 9 = 13
4) 1 + 9 = 10
5) 4 + 1 = 5
6) 8 + 2 = 10
7) 2 + 8 = 10
8) 1 + 3 = 4
9) 9 + 2 = 11
10) 7 + 9 = 16
11) 5 + 3 = 8
12) 4 + 2 = 6
13) 1 + 1 = 2
14) 8 + 5 = 13
15) 2 + 9 = 11
16) 6 + 2 = 8
17) 3 + 6 = 9
18) 7 + 6 = 13
19) 9 + 5 = 14
20) 6 + 1 = 7

Addition Facts

Add.

1) 4 + 5 = 9
2) 3 + 9 = 12
3) 4 + 8 = 12
4) 1 + 6 = 7
5) 2 + 4 = 6
6) 5 + 6 = 11
7) 8 + 5 = 13
8) 5 + 2 = 7
9) 2 + 5 = 7
10) 9 + 5 = 14
11) 1 + 3 = 4
12) 3 + 5 = 8
13) 3 + 2 = 5
14) 9 + 2 = 11
15) 3 + 1 = 4
16) 4 + 2 = 6
17) 2 + 3 = 5
18) 7 + 6 = 13
19) 4 + 9 = 13
20) 4 + 4 = 8

Subtraction Facts

Subtract.

1) 10 − 5 = 5
2) 6 − 3 = 3
3) 5 − 3 = 2
4) 5 − 2 = 3
5) 2 − 2 = 0
6) 14 − 6 = 8
7) 13 − 5 = 8
8) 6 − 4 = 2
9) 9 − 2 = 7
10) 15 − 8 = 7
11) 18 − 9 = 9
12) 14 − 7 = 7
13) 11 − 8 = 3
14) 5 − 5 = 0
15) 16 − 8 = 8
16) 10 − 9 = 1
17) 3 − 1 = 2
18) 14 − 5 = 9
19) 15 − 6 = 9
20) 4 − 3 = 1

www.claymaze.com

Subtraction Facts

Subtract.

1) 8 − 4 = 4	2) 5 − 2 = 3	3) 14 − 6 = 8	4) 4 − 1 = 3	5) 8 − 7 = 1
6) 15 − 8 = 7	7) 2 − 1 = 1	8) 11 − 9 = 2	9) 16 − 9 = 7	10) 10 − 6 = 4
11) 11 − 8 = 3	12) 18 − 9 = 9	13) 9 − 7 = 2	14) 3 − 1 = 2	15) 5 − 1 = 4
16) 4 − 4 = 0	17) 6 − 2 = 4	18) 12 − 4 = 8	19) 15 − 7 = 8	20) 15 − 6 = 9

Subtraction Facts

Subtract.

1) 17 − 8 = 9	2) 15 − 6 = 9	3) 3 − 3 = 0	4) 3 − 2 = 1	5) 16 − 7 = 9
6) 18 − 9 = 9	7) 13 − 5 = 8	8) 11 − 9 = 2	9) 8 − 3 = 5	10) 8 − 7 = 1
11) 10 − 4 = 6	12) 12 − 8 = 4	13) 3 − 1 = 2	14) 7 − 5 = 2	15) 9 − 6 = 3
16) 16 − 8 = 8	17) 17 − 9 = 8	18) 4 − 3 = 1	19) 11 − 4 = 7	20) 9 − 7 = 2

Subtraction Facts

Subtract.

1) 18 − 9 = 9	2) 2 − 1 = 1	3) 2 − 2 = 0	4) 11 − 4 = 7	5) 6 − 1 = 5
6) 7 − 1 = 6	7) 11 − 5 = 6	8) 10 − 5 = 5	9) 15 − 6 = 9	10) 10 − 8 = 2
11) 11 − 7 = 4	12) 6 − 5 = 1	13) 3 − 3 = 0	14) 15 − 7 = 8	15) 3 − 2 = 1
16) 7 − 3 = 4	17) 10 − 1 = 9	18) 12 − 4 = 8	19) 16 − 9 = 7	20) 17 − 9 = 8

Subtraction Facts

Subtract.

1) 2 − 1 = 1	2) 15 − 7 = 8	3) 12 − 6 = 6	4) 12 − 8 = 4	5) 9 − 7 = 2
6) 3 − 3 = 0	7) 6 − 1 = 5	8) 10 − 5 = 5	9) 11 − 6 = 5	10) 16 − 8 = 8
11) 7 − 3 = 4	12) 7 − 6 = 1	13) 8 − 1 = 7	14) 9 − 9 = 0	15) 11 − 9 = 2
16) 6 − 5 = 1	17) 14 − 6 = 8	18) 8 − 4 = 4	19) 10 − 4 = 6	20) 14 − 8 = 6

Subtraction Facts

Subtract.

1) 4 − 3 = 1	2) 18 − 9 = 9	3) 13 − 5 = 8	4) 3 − 1 = 2	5) 9 − 2 = 7
6) 13 − 4 = 9	7) 12 − 5 = 7	8) 12 − 6 = 6	9) 2 − 2 = 0	10) 8 − 6 = 2
11) 15 − 9 = 6	12) 17 − 8 = 9	13) 13 − 8 = 5	14) 15 − 7 = 8	15) 16 − 7 = 9
16) 14 − 7 = 7	17) 12 − 4 = 8	18) 5 − 2 = 3	19) 4 − 1 = 3	20) 15 − 6 = 9

Subtraction Facts

Subtract.

1) 3 − 3 = 0	2) 4 − 2 = 2	3) 18 − 9 = 9	4) 15 − 9 = 6	5) 9 − 8 = 1
6) 17 − 8 = 9	7) 3 − 2 = 1	8) 12 − 4 = 8	9) 14 − 7 = 7	10) 14 − 5 = 9
11) 8 − 6 = 2	12) 7 − 4 = 3	13) 6 − 5 = 1	14) 15 − 7 = 8	15) 16 − 7 = 9
16) 10 − 5 = 5	17) 15 − 8 = 7	18) 12 − 9 = 3	19) 5 − 4 = 1	20) 13 − 9 = 4

www.claymaze.com

Subtraction Facts

Subtract.

1) 14 − 9 = 5	2) 4 − 2 = 2	3) 12 − 3 = 9	4) 12 − 8 = 4	5) 17 − 9 = 8
6) 4 − 1 = 3	7) 16 − 9 = 7	8) 5 − 4 = 1	9) 13 − 9 = 4	10) 13 − 6 = 7
11) 7 − 5 = 2	12) 8 − 1 = 7	13) 12 − 7 = 5	14) 14 − 8 = 6	15) 4 − 3 = 1
16) 8 − 2 = 6	17) 12 − 5 = 7	18) 15 − 9 = 6	19) 7 − 2 = 5	20) 14 − 6 = 8

Subtraction Facts

Subtract.

1) 12 − 6 = 6	2) 7 − 7 = 0	3) 11 − 7 = 4	4) 7 − 4 = 3	5) 12 − 8 = 4
6) 18 − 9 = 9	7) 13 − 7 = 6	8) 2 − 2 = 0	9) 7 − 1 = 6	10) 9 − 8 = 1
11) 10 − 6 = 4	12) 10 − 9 = 1	13) 17 − 9 = 8	14) 11 − 2 = 9	15) 11 − 9 = 2
16) 15 − 6 = 9	17) 16 − 8 = 8	18) 8 − 6 = 2	19) 6 − 1 = 5	20) 12 − 9 = 3

Subtraction Facts

Subtract.

1) 14 − 9 = 5	2) 16 − 7 = 9	3) 3 − 2 = 1	4) 13 − 6 = 7	5) 5 − 4 = 1
6) 10 − 6 = 4	7) 17 − 8 = 9	8) 18 − 9 = 9	9) 2 − 1 = 1	10) 3 − 1 = 2
11) 4 − 1 = 3	12) 16 − 9 = 7	13) 8 − 4 = 4	14) 2 − 2 = 0	15) 4 − 2 = 2
16) 14 − 5 = 9	17) 8 − 7 = 1	18) 14 − 8 = 6	19) 11 − 6 = 5	20) 6 − 2 = 4

Subtraction Facts

Subtract.

1) 15 − 7 = 8	2) 7 − 6 = 1	3) 16 − 8 = 8	4) 15 − 9 = 6	5) 12 − 7 = 5
6) 13 − 6 = 7	7) 5 − 4 = 1	8) 16 − 9 = 7	9) 9 − 8 = 1	10) 10 − 1 = 9
11) 10 − 7 = 3	12) 3 − 3 = 0	13) 9 − 1 = 8	14) 9 − 6 = 3	15) 6 − 1 = 5
16) 6 − 4 = 2	17) 15 − 6 = 9	18) 15 − 8 = 7	19) 4 − 2 = 2	20) 8 − 1 = 7

2 Digit Addition No Regrouping

Add.

1) 22 + 14 = 36	2) 15 + 12 = 27	3) 18 + 11 = 29	4) 45 + 21 = 66
5) 34 + 10 = 44	6) 47 + 42 = 89	7) 57 + 41 = 98	8) 31 + 27 = 58
9) 13 + 10 = 23	10) 52 + 36 = 88	11) 61 + 32 = 93	12) 11 + 11 = 22
13) 41 + 20 = 61	14) 21 + 21 = 42	15) 12 + 11 = 23	16) 30 + 20 = 50

2 Digit Addition No Regrouping

Add.

1) 43 + 24 = 67	2) 14 + 13 = 27	3) 60 + 22 = 82	4) 74 + 21 = 95
5) 57 + 32 = 89	6) 24 + 14 = 38	7) 51 + 18 = 69	8) 44 + 43 = 87
9) 27 + 21 = 48	10) 31 + 31 = 62	11) 17 + 10 = 27	12) 41 + 36 = 77
13) 21 + 17 = 38	14) 10 + 10 = 20	15) 12 + 12 = 24	16) 11 + 11 = 22

www.claymaze.com

2 Digit Addition No Regrouping

Add.

1) 38 + 30 = 68
2) 21 + 11 = 32
3) 43 + 13 = 56
4) 35 + 21 = 56

5) 26 + 13 = 39
6) 60 + 11 = 71
7) 11 + 11 = 22
8) 50 + 38 = 88

9) 29 + 10 = 39
10) 30 + 10 = 40
11) 54 + 30 = 84
12) 67 + 31 = 98

13) 12 + 12 = 24
14) 42 + 42 = 84
15) 15 + 12 = 27
16) 40 + 31 = 71

2 Digit Addition No Regrouping

Add.

1) 24 + 13 = 37
2) 34 + 23 = 57
3) 51 + 16 = 67
4) 25 + 20 = 45

5) 41 + 33 = 74
6) 29 + 10 = 39
7) 84 + 15 = 99
8) 50 + 16 = 66

9) 27 + 21 = 48
10) 26 + 13 = 39
11) 43 + 20 = 63
12) 20 + 11 = 31

13) 15 + 11 = 26
14) 66 + 11 = 77
15) 52 + 35 = 87
16) 47 + 40 = 87

2 Digit Addition No Regrouping

Add.

1) 47 + 40 = 87
2) 42 + 15 = 57
3) 11 + 10 = 21
4) 71 + 23 = 94

5) 74 + 22 = 96
6) 15 + 13 = 28
7) 36 + 21 = 57
8) 30 + 16 = 46

9) 52 + 36 = 88
10) 75 + 23 = 98
11) 53 + 12 = 65
12) 61 + 37 = 98

13) 10 + 10 = 20
14) 62 + 26 = 88
15) 63 + 24 = 87
16) 45 + 31 = 76

2 Digit Addition No Regrouping

Add.

1) 45 + 42 = 87
2) 31 + 25 = 56
3) 74 + 14 = 88
4) 21 + 13 = 34

5) 36 + 30 = 66
6) 24 + 24 = 48
7) 30 + 29 = 59
8) 35 + 33 = 68

9) 32 + 14 = 46
10) 43 + 23 = 66
11) 51 + 34 = 85
12) 11 + 11 = 22

13) 40 + 40 = 80
14) 44 + 40 = 84
15) 41 + 21 = 62
16) 52 + 31 = 83

2 Digit Addition No Regrouping

Add.

1) 45 + 43 = 88
2) 52 + 47 = 99
3) 65 + 30 = 95
4) 31 + 17 = 48

5) 71 + 13 = 84
6) 58 + 20 = 78
7) 60 + 16 = 76
8) 19 + 10 = 29

9) 42 + 23 = 65
10) 24 + 14 = 38
11) 22 + 12 = 34
12) 30 + 24 = 54

13) 40 + 30 = 70
14) 44 + 10 = 54
15) 66 + 32 = 98
16) 73 + 26 = 99

2 Digit Addition No Regrouping

Add.

1) 50 + 30 = 80
2) 71 + 25 = 96
3) 35 + 11 = 46
4) 11 + 11 = 22

5) 70 + 10 = 80
6) 20 + 15 = 35
7) 58 + 11 = 69
8) 53 + 23 = 76

9) 45 + 24 = 69
10) 69 + 20 = 89
11) 30 + 18 = 48
12) 63 + 35 = 98

13) 33 + 25 = 58
14) 34 + 31 = 65
15) 13 + 13 = 26
16) 21 + 12 = 33

www.claymaze.com

PAGE: 34

2 Digit Addition — No Regrouping

Add.

1) 72 +10 82	2) 46 +42 88	3) 20 +10 30	4) 57 +42 99
5) 33 +22 55	6) 37 +20 57	7) 26 +11 37	8) 13 +11 24
9) 34 +20 54	10) 78 +10 88	11) 51 +10 61	12) 10 +10 20
13) 14 +12 26	14) 50 +10 60	15) 16 +13 29	16) 29 +10 39

PAGE: 35

2 Digit Addition — No Regrouping

Add.

1) 52 +44 96	2) 50 +36 86	3) 47 +22 69	4) 63 +35 98
5) 73 +10 83	6) 71 +22 93	7) 20 +17 37	8) 31 +11 42
9) 12 +11 23	10) 44 +20 64	11) 43 +22 65	12) 22 +15 37
13) 76 +12 88	14) 18 +10 28	15) 60 +29 89	16) 24 +10 34

PAGE: 36

2 Digit Addition — No Regrouping

Add.

1) 30 +12 42	2) 62 +36 98	3) 32 +32 64	4) 25 +12 37
5) 31 +17 48	6) 17 +11 28	7) 66 +13 79	8) 15 +14 29
9) 44 +20 64	10) 22 +15 37	11) 46 +33 79	12) 48 +20 68
13) 16 +11 27	14) 57 +30 87	15) 40 +22 62	16) 23 +14 37

PAGE: 38

2 Digit Addition — With Regrouping

Add.

1) 28 +13 41	2) 58 +26 84	3) 99 +98 197	4) 93 +78 171
5) 29 +14 43	6) 45 +29 74	7) 17 +15 32	8) 19 +18 37
9) 26 +26 52	10) 34 +29 63	11) 55 +19 74	12) 75 +38 113
13) 27 +18 45	14) 86 +77 163	15) 84 +27 111	16) 68 +45 113

PAGE: 39

2 Digit Addition — With Regrouping

Add.

1) 69 +25 94	2) 77 +35 112	3) 59 +45 104	4) 78 +26 104
5) 88 +85 173	6) 58 +33 91	7) 27 +24 51	8) 48 +44 92
9) 19 +19 38	10) 49 +22 71	11) 39 +32 71	12) 57 +28 85
13) 37 +28 65	14) 38 +33 71	15) 29 +27 56	16) 56 +39 95

PAGE: 40

2 Digit Addition — With Regrouping

Add.

1) 16 +15 31	2) 94 +49 143	3) 46 +35 81	4) 58 +18 76
5) 29 +17 46	6) 47 +19 66	7) 38 +15 53	8) 43 +28 71
9) 79 +45 124	10) 88 +66 154	11) 28 +28 56	12) 57 +45 102
13) 19 +15 34	14) 65 +46 111	15) 97 +27 124	16) 82 +69 151

PAGE: 41

2 Digit Addition | With Regrouping
Add.

1) 48 + 19 = 67	2) 29 + 24 = 53	3) 98 + 35 = 133	4) 46 + 17 = 63
5) 44 + 17 = 61	6) 39 + 13 = 52	7) 76 + 36 = 112	8) 95 + 38 = 133
9) 54 + 39 = 93	10) 59 + 27 = 86	11) 97 + 65 = 162	12) 16 + 16 = 32
13) 67 + 45 = 112	14) 19 + 12 = 31	15) 69 + 59 = 128	16) 58 + 18 = 76

PAGE: 42

2 Digit Addition | With Regrouping
Add.

1) 99 + 18 = 117	2) 67 + 44 = 111	3) 77 + 77 = 154	4) 96 + 68 = 164
5) 86 + 59 = 145	6) 49 + 45 = 94	7) 97 + 68 = 165	8) 94 + 77 = 171
9) 79 + 69 = 148	10) 59 + 26 = 85	11) 95 + 56 = 151	12) 54 + 17 = 71
13) 29 + 19 = 48	14) 89 + 53 = 142	15) 74 + 29 = 103	16) 19 + 12 = 31

PAGE: 43

2 Digit Addition | With Regrouping
Add.

1) 29 + 13 = 42	2) 19 + 16 = 35	3) 58 + 19 = 77	4) 98 + 54 = 152
5) 77 + 35 = 112	6) 48 + 29 = 77	7) 76 + 37 = 113	8) 99 + 78 = 177
9) 47 + 16 = 63	10) 52 + 49 = 101	11) 79 + 47 = 126	12) 32 + 29 = 61
13) 38 + 25 = 63	14) 16 + 15 = 31	15) 55 + 29 = 84	16) 75 + 69 = 144

PAGE: 44

2 Digit Addition | With Regrouping
Add.

1) 85 + 56 = 141	2) 18 + 14 = 32	3) 23 + 19 = 42	4) 28 + 24 = 52
5) 96 + 19 = 115	6) 19 + 17 = 36	7) 97 + 64 = 161	8) 56 + 16 = 72
9) 89 + 54 = 143	10) 68 + 46 = 114	11) 72 + 49 = 121	12) 37 + 25 = 62
13) 77 + 28 = 105	14) 84 + 77 = 161	15) 98 + 25 = 123	16) 24 + 18 = 42

PAGE: 45

2 Digit Addition | With Regrouping
Add.

1) 95 + 48 = 143	2) 18 + 17 = 35	3) 99 + 29 = 128	4) 65 + 39 = 104
5) 83 + 78 = 161	6) 17 + 14 = 31	7) 82 + 39 = 121	8) 67 + 37 = 104
9) 66 + 38 = 104	10) 49 + 27 = 76	11) 79 + 22 = 101	12) 48 + 36 = 84
13) 46 + 18 = 64	14) 29 + 24 = 53	15) 28 + 27 = 55	16) 19 + 14 = 33

PAGE: 46

2 Digit Addition | With Regrouping
Add.

1) 84 + 69 = 153	2) 37 + 15 = 52	3) 88 + 88 = 176	4) 97 + 25 = 122
5) 39 + 19 = 58	6) 96 + 18 = 114	7) 33 + 18 = 51	8) 86 + 65 = 151
9) 17 + 14 = 31	10) 76 + 38 = 114	11) 98 + 35 = 133	12) 49 + 34 = 83
13) 68 + 35 = 103	14) 94 + 17 = 111	15) 56 + 56 = 112	16) 42 + 39 = 81

www.claymaze.com

2 Digit Addition With Regrouping

Add.

1) 78
+38
——
116

2) 99
+43
——
142

3) 26
+25
——
51

4) 56
+29
——
85

5) 38
+18
——
56

6) 44
+19
——
63

7) 68
+58
——
126

8) 58
+56
——
114

9) 57
+35
——
92

10) 37
+35
——
72

11) 46
+29
——
75

12) 89
+25
——
114

13) 97
+39
——
136

14) 62
+59
——
121

15) 75
+36
——
111

16) 63
+29
——
92

2 Digit Addition With Regrouping

Add.

1) 37
+35
——
72

2) 33
+29
——
62

3) 47
+37
——
84

4) 89
+82
——
171

5) 85
+56
——
141

6) 59
+37
——
96

7) 94
+87
——
181

8) 54
+37
——
91

9) 44
+17
——
61

10) 45
+26
——
71

11) 27
+18
——
45

12) 18
+14
——
32

13) 43
+28
——
71

14) 39
+17
——
56

15) 49
+12
——
61

16) 28
+14
——
42

2 Digit Subtraction No Regrouping

Subtract.

1) 69
-37
——
32

2) 99
-45
——
54

3) 89
-75
——
14

4) 32
-10
——
22

5) 29
-11
——
18

6) 49
-36
——
13

7) 46
-15
——
31

8) 34
-33
——
1

9) 24
-10
——
14

10) 88
-31
——
57

11) 56
-33
——
23

12) 16
-14
——
2

13) 78
-56
——
22

14) 54
-21
——
33

15) 52
-50
——
2

16) 12
-11
——
1

2 Digit Subtraction No Regrouping

Subtract.

1) 77
-51
——
26

2) 79
-41
——
38

3) 16
-14
——
2

4) 27
-20
——
7

5) 24
-11
——
13

6) 49
-34
——
15

7) 19
-12
——
7

8) 11
-10
——
1

9) 67
-32
——
35

10) 39
-33
——
6

11) 59
-45
——
14

12) 69
-65
——
4

13) 98
-75
——
23

14) 76
-42
——
34

15) 68
-33
——
35

16) 48
-26
——
22

2 Digit Subtraction No Regrouping

Subtract.

1) 77
-24
——
53

2) 43
-31
——
12

3) 26
-15
——
11

4) 81
-60
——
21

5) 47
-31
——
16

6) 52
-11
——
41

7) 79
-27
——
52

8) 36
-12
——
24

9) 75
-13
——
62

10) 92
-31
——
61

11) 88
-43
——
45

12) 84
-42
——
42

13) 99
-17
——
82

14) 11
-10
——
1

15) 97
-30
——
67

16) 72
-31
——
41

2 Digit Subtraction No Regrouping

Subtract.

1) 78
-23
——
55

2) 95
-81
——
14

3) 67
-40
——
27

4) 27
-23
——
4

5) 35
-20
——
15

6) 87
-70
——
17

7) 79
-40
——
39

8) 69
-56
——
13

9) 99
-60
——
39

10) 92
-10
——
82

11) 34
-11
——
23

12) 12
-11
——
1

13) 84
-43
——
41

14) 29
-21
——
8

15) 39
-23
——
16

16) 48
-43
——
5

www.claymaze.com

PAGE: 54

2 Digit Subtraction — No Regrouping

Subtract.

1) 64 − 53 = 11	2) 96 − 81 = 15	3) 45 − 11 = 34	4) 66 − 65 = 1
5) 48 − 34 = 14	6) 27 − 25 = 2	7) 28 − 11 = 17	8) 69 − 34 = 35
9) 79 − 61 = 18	10) 19 − 16 = 3	11) 99 − 64 = 35	12) 24 − 20 = 4
13) 89 − 11 = 78	14) 16 − 15 = 1	15) 37 − 20 = 17	16) 35 − 10 = 25

PAGE: 55

2 Digit Subtraction — No Regrouping

Subtract.

1) 99 − 71 = 28	2) 89 − 50 = 39	3) 56 − 52 = 4	4) 41 − 10 = 31
5) 24 − 22 = 2	6) 18 − 15 = 3	7) 77 − 30 = 47	8) 83 − 52 = 31
9) 46 − 24 = 22	10) 59 − 17 = 42	11) 97 − 81 = 16	12) 17 − 15 = 2
13) 96 − 53 = 43	14) 37 − 34 = 3	15) 16 − 14 = 2	16) 87 − 61 = 26

PAGE: 56

2 Digit Subtraction — No Regrouping

Subtract.

1) 38 − 17 = 21	2) 54 − 30 = 24	3) 86 − 13 = 73	4) 14 − 13 = 1
5) 15 − 11 = 4	6) 27 − 22 = 5	7) 34 − 10 = 24	8) 99 − 35 = 64
9) 48 − 25 = 23	10) 47 − 42 = 5	11) 57 − 41 = 16	12) 95 − 70 = 25
13) 89 − 68 = 21	14) 13 − 10 = 3	15) 28 − 17 = 11	16) 49 − 23 = 26

PAGE: 57

2 Digit Subtraction — No Regrouping

Subtract.

1) 28 − 10 = 18	2) 15 − 13 = 2	3) 65 − 30 = 35	4) 58 − 44 = 14
5) 78 − 70 = 8	6) 18 − 12 = 6	7) 38 − 37 = 1	8) 48 − 27 = 21
9) 83 − 30 = 53	10) 23 − 12 = 11	11) 73 − 70 = 3	12) 89 − 22 = 67
13) 53 − 22 = 31	14) 98 − 53 = 45	15) 17 − 14 = 3	16) 47 − 32 = 15

PAGE: 58

2 Digit Subtraction — No Regrouping

Subtract.

1) 43 − 11 = 32	2) 67 − 20 = 47	3) 12 − 10 = 2	4) 28 − 14 = 14
5) 96 − 44 = 52	6) 92 − 31 = 61	7) 65 − 22 = 43	8) 68 − 44 = 24
9) 93 − 80 = 13	10) 87 − 35 = 52	11) 75 − 50 = 25	12) 39 − 35 = 4
13) 89 − 12 = 77	14) 19 − 15 = 4	15) 38 − 25 = 13	16) 86 − 64 = 22

PAGE: 59

2 Digit Subtraction — No Regrouping

Subtract.

1) 66 − 21 = 45	2) 39 − 18 = 21	3) 92 − 50 = 42	4) 37 − 21 = 16
5) 35 − 34 = 1	6) 69 − 63 = 6	7) 59 − 28 = 31	8) 57 − 56 = 1
9) 38 − 10 = 28	10) 17 − 14 = 3	11) 58 − 34 = 24	12) 94 − 51 = 43
13) 43 − 11 = 32	14) 76 − 45 = 31	15) 85 − 42 = 43	16) 32 − 20 = 12

www.claymaze.com

2 Digit Subtraction No Regrouping

Subtract.

1) 73 − 41 = 32	2) 67 − 54 = 13	3) 25 − 13 = 12	4) 17 − 14 = 3
5) 68 − 14 = 54	6) 66 − 11 = 55	7) 33 − 10 = 23	8) 75 − 51 = 24
9) 37 − 32 = 5	10) 89 − 70 = 19	11) 15 − 14 = 1	12) 12 − 11 = 1
13) 88 − 23 = 65	14) 24 − 10 = 14	15) 27 − 21 = 6	16) 96 − 22 = 74

2 Digit Subtraction With Regrouping

Subtract.

1) 34 − 27 = 7	2) 80 − 23 = 57	3) 67 − 48 = 19	4) 90 − 89 = 1
5) 72 − 34 = 38	6) 33 − 25 = 8	7) 20 − 19 = 1	8) 65 − 39 = 26
9) 52 − 19 = 33	10) 87 − 38 = 49	11) 41 − 19 = 22	12) 54 − 15 = 39
13) 82 − 75 = 7	14) 60 − 48 = 12	15) 23 − 17 = 6	16) 30 − 18 = 12

2 Digit Subtraction With Regrouping

Subtract.

1) 61 − 49 = 12	2) 60 − 22 = 38	3) 47 − 18 = 29	4) 83 − 27 = 56
5) 63 − 15 = 48	6) 31 − 18 = 13	7) 92 − 56 = 36	8) 97 − 89 = 8
9) 71 − 39 = 32	10) 41 − 29 = 12	11) 81 − 16 = 65	12) 91 − 23 = 68
13) 66 − 49 = 17	14) 52 − 27 = 25	15) 94 − 27 = 67	16) 30 − 11 = 19

2 Digit Subtraction With Regrouping

Subtract.

1) 78 − 59 = 19	2) 25 − 19 = 6	3) 91 − 62 = 29	4) 75 − 58 = 17
5) 31 − 12 = 19	6) 44 − 29 = 15	7) 71 − 14 = 57	8) 23 − 17 = 6
9) 51 − 48 = 3	10) 90 − 34 = 56	11) 92 − 29 = 63	12) 60 − 45 = 15
13) 34 − 19 = 15	14) 81 − 68 = 13	15) 73 − 45 = 28	16) 70 − 55 = 15

2 Digit Subtraction With Regrouping

Subtract.

1) 83 − 15 = 68	2) 63 − 38 = 25	3) 40 − 13 = 27	4) 50 − 23 = 27
5) 71 − 65 = 6	6) 60 − 27 = 33	7) 22 − 17 = 5	8) 72 − 67 = 5
9) 70 − 53 = 17	10) 41 − 16 = 25	11) 92 − 85 = 7	12) 74 − 15 = 59
13) 75 − 36 = 39	14) 61 − 25 = 36	15) 43 − 35 = 8	16) 64 − 19 = 45

2 Digit Subtraction With Regrouping

Subtract.

1) 64 − 18 = 46	2) 31 − 23 = 8	3) 50 − 19 = 31	4) 81 − 16 = 65
5) 53 − 34 = 19	6) 84 − 48 = 36	7) 51 − 16 = 35	8) 23 − 17 = 6
9) 90 − 52 = 38	10) 33 − 15 = 18	11) 56 − 19 = 37	12) 43 − 15 = 28
13) 41 − 39 = 2	14) 46 − 29 = 17	15) 83 − 24 = 59	16) 55 − 46 = 9

2 Digit Subtraction With Regrouping

Subtract.

1) 50
− 45
5

2) 52
− 17
35

3) 41
− 27
14

4) 71
− 18
53

5) 80
− 22
58

6) 62
− 13
49

7) 53
− 14
39

8) 63
− 27
36

9) 30
− 11
19

10) 33
− 25
8

11) 83
− 17
66

12) 90
− 26
64

13) 60
− 11
49

14) 31
− 15
16

15) 23
− 18
5

16) 96
− 17
79

2 Digit Subtraction With Regrouping

Subtract.

1) 87
− 48
39

2) 31
− 26
5

3) 96
− 67
29

4) 63
− 24
39

5) 74
− 26
48

6) 80
− 36
44

7) 21
− 15
6

8) 24
− 18
6

9) 28
− 19
9

10) 70
− 44
26

11) 82
− 67
15

12) 34
− 27
7

13) 90
− 89
1

14) 72
− 34
38

15) 62
− 27
35

16) 84
− 29
55

2 Digit Subtraction With Regrouping

Subtract.

1) 52
− 36
16

2) 81
− 63
18

3) 46
− 27
19

4) 76
− 58
18

5) 55
− 16
39

6) 72
− 27
45

7) 96
− 57
39

8) 24
− 17
7

9) 47
− 19
28

10) 23
− 14
9

11) 51
− 29
22

12) 41
− 39
2

13) 36
− 18
18

14) 75
− 59
16

15) 80
− 42
38

16) 42
− 24
18

2 Digit Subtraction With Regrouping

Subtract.

1) 72
− 48
24

2) 82
− 43
39

3) 60
− 52
8

4) 65
− 18
47

5) 43
− 18
25

6) 40
− 28
12

7) 83
− 17
66

8) 33
− 25
8

9) 31
− 14
17

10) 93
− 18
75

11) 90
− 14
76

12) 36
− 28
8

13) 21
− 16
5

14) 62
− 46
16

15) 30
− 29
1

16) 45
− 36
9

2 Digit Subtraction With Regrouping

Subtract.

1) 93
− 35
58

2) 90
− 76
14

3) 43
− 37
6

4) 75
− 29
46

5) 44
− 38
6

6) 62
− 59
3

7) 74
− 15
59

8) 41
− 19
22

9) 45
− 37
8

10) 42
− 37
5

11) 30
− 19
11

12) 22
− 19
3

13) 20
− 16
4

14) 95
− 49
46

15) 87
− 48
39

16) 61
− 28
33

2 Digit Subtraction With Regrouping

Subtract.

1) 80
− 64
16

2) 50
− 14
36

3) 22
− 14
8

4) 61
− 26
35

5) 40
− 29
11

6) 70
− 38
32

7) 91
− 32
59

8) 54
− 29
25

9) 42
− 25
17

10) 51
− 43
8

11) 62
− 16
46

12) 34
− 17
17

13) 95
− 26
69

14) 30
− 14
16

15) 96
− 78
18

16) 71
− 63
8

www.claymaze.com

3 Digit Addition No Regrouping

Add.

1) 222 +153 375	2) 643 +326 969	3) 361 +510 871	4) 214 +464 678
5) 462 +100 562	6) 524 +303 827	7) 572 +217 789	8) 745 +234 979
9) 423 +156 579	10) 337 +262 599	11) 353 +301 654	12) 522 +112 634
13) 237 +661 898	14) 704 +275 979	15) 152 +641 793	16) 274 +501 775

3 Digit Addition No Regrouping

Add.

1) 472 +127 599	2) 413 +281 694	3) 229 +540 769	4) 534 +350 884
5) 261 +123 384	6) 337 +350 687	7) 318 +651 969	8) 301 +613 914
9) 254 +522 776	10) 501 +335 836	11) 415 +353 768	12) 520 +414 934
13) 303 +170 473	14) 120 +335 455	15) 102 +104 206	16) 130 +153 283

3 Digit Addition No Regrouping

Add.

1) 665 +211 876	2) 125 +561 686	3) 396 +102 498	4) 422 +427 849
5) 415 +472 887	6) 526 +261 787	7) 260 +623 883	8) 142 +246 388
9) 183 +204 387	10) 408 +340 748	11) 199 +800 999	12) 202 +340 542
13) 480 +102 582	14) 620 +307 927	15) 123 +224 347	16) 822 +164 986

3 Digit Addition No Regrouping

Add.

1) 732 +204 936	2) 131 +667 798	3) 617 +210 827	4) 321 +572 893
5) 438 +200 638	6) 201 +611 812	7) 215 +281 496	8) 706 +233 939
9) 354 +524 878	10) 503 +444 947	11) 740 +122 862	12) 641 +343 984
13) 607 +100 707	14) 124 +421 545	15) 142 +334 476	16) 335 +622 957

3 Digit Addition No Regrouping

Add.

1) 474 +401 875	2) 146 +623 769	3) 367 +122 489	4) 655 +133 788
5) 407 +232 639	6) 177 +420 597	7) 212 +335 547	8) 231 +757 988
9) 450 +533 983	10) 207 +281 488	11) 751 +226 977	12) 612 +186 798
13) 294 +403 697	14) 374 +103 477	15) 306 +173 479	16) 124 +364 488

3 Digit Addition No Regrouping

Add.

1) 102 +510 612	2) 640 +235 875	3) 316 +460 776	4) 344 +534 878
5) 305 +502 807	6) 331 +650 981	7) 566 +313 879	8) 760 +221 981
9) 604 +211 815	10) 601 +171 772	11) 170 +117 287	12) 217 +650 867
13) 281 +514 795	14) 109 +840 949	15) 276 +522 798	16) 481 +210 691

www.claymaze.com

3 Digit Addition No Regrouping

Add.

1) 259 +400 = 659	2) 365 +222 = 587	3) 431 +163 = 594	4) 273 +513 = 786
5) 607 +220 = 827	6) 574 +320 = 894	7) 318 +100 = 418	8) 241 +721 = 962
9) 639 +240 = 879	10) 550 +103 = 653	11) 714 +150 = 864	12) 163 +225 = 388
13) 346 +200 = 546	14) 326 +221 = 547	15) 260 +103 = 363	16) 752 +220 = 972

3 Digit Addition No Regrouping

Add.

1) 754 +120 = 874	2) 897 +100 = 997	3) 610 +343 = 953	4) 520 +154 = 674
5) 541 +451 = 992	6) 612 +275 = 887	7) 221 +216 = 437	8) 421 +167 = 588
9) 120 +678 = 798	10) 273 +310 = 583	11) 323 +415 = 738	12) 145 +343 = 488
13) 680 +116 = 796	14) 313 +680 = 993	15) 501 +252 = 753	16) 271 +207 = 478

3 Digit Addition No Regrouping

Add.

1) 103 +473 = 576	2) 331 +561 = 892	3) 517 +260 = 777	4) 467 +332 = 799
5) 860 +139 = 999	6) 205 +203 = 408	7) 270 +707 = 977	8) 372 +525 = 897
9) 291 +103 = 394	10) 471 +215 = 686	11) 230 +534 = 764	12) 512 +351 = 863
13) 223 +174 = 397	14) 362 +302 = 664	15) 506 +390 = 896	16) 544 +231 = 775

3 Digit Addition No Regrouping

Add.

1) 201 +200 = 401	2) 741 +142 = 883	3) 250 +342 = 592	4) 430 +314 = 744
5) 414 +275 = 689	6) 133 +853 = 986	7) 304 +133 = 437	8) 431 +365 = 796
9) 260 +629 = 889	10) 641 +312 = 953	11) 282 +217 = 499	12) 157 +201 = 358
13) 153 +401 = 554	14) 651 +333 = 984	15) 480 +216 = 696	16) 510 +482 = 992

3 Digit Addition No Regrouping

Add.

1) 112 +417 = 529	2) 242 +715 = 957	3) 800 +190 = 990	4) 276 +402 = 678
5) 605 +320 = 925	6) 115 +571 = 686	7) 134 +765 = 899	8) 230 +706 = 936
9) 532 +310 = 842	10) 791 +107 = 898	11) 801 +128 = 929	12) 450 +444 = 894
13) 410 +386 = 796	14) 284 +700 = 984	15) 415 +150 = 565	16) 674 +301 = 975

3 Digit Addition With Regrouping

Add.

1) 386 +492 = 878	2) 343 +888 = 1231	3) 942 +587 = 1529	4) 552 +783 = 1335
5) 563 +741 = 1304	6) 262 +757 = 1019	7) 123 +629 = 752	8) 156 +556 = 712
9) 190 +190 = 380	10) 970 +370 = 1340	11) 334 +196 = 530	12) 962 +452 = 1414
13) 179 +638 = 817	14) 168 +337 = 505	15) 699 +132 = 831	16) 225 +308 = 533

www.claymaze.com

3 Digit Addition With Regrouping

Add.

1) 185 +218 = 403
2) 987 +809 = 1796
3) 451 +667 = 1118
4) 486 +874 = 1360

5) 651 +656 = 1307
6) 891 +576 = 1467
7) 943 +176 = 1119
8) 166 +608 = 774

9) 386 +955 = 1341
10) 586 +272 = 858
11) 284 +960 = 1244
12) 209 +441 = 650

13) 272 +836 = 1108
14) 245 +636 = 881
15) 434 +780 = 1214
16) 554 +829 = 1383

3 Digit Addition With Regrouping

Add.

1) 490 +383 = 873
2) 946 +673 = 1619
3) 592 +113 = 705
4) 380 +849 = 1229

5) 447 +727 = 1174
6) 789 +264 = 1053
7) 138 +622 = 760
8) 233 +689 = 922

9) 199 +446 = 645
10) 717 +394 = 1111
11) 613 +409 = 1022
12) 818 +998 = 1816

13) 396 +685 = 1081
14) 555 +792 = 1347
15) 256 +391 = 647
16) 484 +796 = 1280

3 Digit Addition With Regrouping

Add.

1) 662 +577 = 1239
2) 563 +976 = 1539
3) 297 +615 = 912
4) 658 +636 = 1294

5) 866 +365 = 1231
6) 945 +685 = 1630
7) 779 +648 = 1427
8) 787 +858 = 1645

9) 796 +536 = 1332
10) 719 +902 = 1621
11) 326 +449 = 775
12) 824 +116 = 940

13) 129 +361 = 490
14) 739 +944 = 1683
15) 513 +694 = 1207
16) 546 +885 = 1431

3 Digit Addition With Regrouping

Add.

1) 439 +518 = 957
2) 780 +586 = 1366
3) 215 +256 = 471
4) 601 +779 = 1380

5) 391 +922 = 1313
6) 925 +466 = 1391
7) 483 +719 = 1202
8) 580 +254 = 834

9) 766 +181 = 947
10) 471 +684 = 1155
11) 674 +181 = 855
12) 627 +205 = 832

13) 672 +661 = 1333
14) 323 +295 = 618
15) 569 +816 = 1385
16) 838 +405 = 1243

3 Digit Addition With Regrouping

Add.

1) 275 +964 = 1239
2) 758 +352 = 1110
3) 743 +593 = 1336
4) 968 +387 = 1355

5) 164 +999 = 1163
6) 185 +370 = 555
7) 974 +696 = 1670
8) 674 +498 = 1172

9) 155 +827 = 982
10) 593 +456 = 1049
11) 551 +154 = 705
12) 250 +665 = 915

13) 446 +675 = 1121
14) 404 +197 = 601
15) 374 +337 = 711
16) 465 +375 = 840

3 Digit Addition With Regrouping

Add.

1) 292 +269 = 561
2) 218 +119 = 337
3) 753 +183 = 936
4) 758 +175 = 933

5) 319 +292 = 611
6) 870 +280 = 1150
7) 899 +812 = 1711
8) 694 +337 = 1031

9) 994 +618 = 1612
10) 638 +563 = 1201
11) 393 +270 = 663
12) 238 +218 = 456

13) 441 +792 = 1233
14) 293 +986 = 1279
15) 846 +381 = 1227
16) 786 +775 = 1561

www.claymaze.com

3 Digit Addition With Regrouping

Add.

1) 125
  + 618
  ————
   743

2) 499
  + 524
  ————
  1023

3) 740
  + 382
  ————
  1122

4) 145
  + 369
  ————
   514

5) 181
  + 741
  ————
   922

6) 262
  + 440
  ————
   702

7) 595
  + 907
  ————
  1502

8) 684
  + 727
  ————
  1411

9) 194
  + 511
  ————
   705

10) 768
  + 404
  ————
  1172

11) 517
  + 754
  ————
  1271

12) 374
  + 483
  ————
   857

13) 808
  + 894
  ————
  1702

14) 236
  + 318
  ————
   554

15) 523
  + 137
  ————
   660

16) 874
  + 252
  ————
  1126

3 Digit Addition With Regrouping

Add.

1) 707
  + 804
  ————
  1511

2) 105
  + 228
  ————
   333

3) 868
  + 203
  ————
  1071

4) 772
  + 262
  ————
  1034

5) 149
  + 809
  ————
   958

6) 768
  + 196
  ————
   964

7) 208
  + 795
  ————
  1003

8) 630
  + 676
  ————
  1306

9) 455
  + 582
  ————
  1037

10) 502
  + 798
  ————
  1300

11) 696
  + 617
  ————
  1313

12) 860
  + 753
  ————
  1613

13) 781
  + 866
  ————
  1647

14) 714
  + 759
  ————
  1473

15) 258
  + 786
  ————
  1044

16) 140
  + 168
  ————
   308

3 Digit Addition With Regrouping

Add.

1) 293
  + 960
  ————
  1253

2) 203
  + 797
  ————
  1000

3) 691
  + 911
  ————
  1602

4) 235
  + 735
  ————
   970

5) 381
  + 578
  ————
   959

6) 428
  + 299
  ————
   727

7) 858
  + 328
  ————
  1186

8) 121
  + 209
  ————
   330

9) 558
  + 167
  ————
   725

10) 585
  + 481
  ————
  1066

11) 299
  + 281
  ————
   580

12) 399
  + 111
  ————
   510

13) 334
  + 107
  ————
   441

14) 648
  + 267
  ————
   915

15) 628
  + 808
  ————
  1436

16) 985
  + 243
  ————
  1228

3 Digit Addition With Regrouping

Add.

1) 710
  + 293
  ————
  1003

2) 118
  + 232
  ————
   350

3) 232
  + 872
  ————
  1104

4) 472
  + 184
  ————
   656

5) 230
  + 274
  ————
   504

6) 444
  + 858
  ————
  1302

7) 676
  + 835
  ————
  1511

8) 682
  + 765
  ————
  1447

9) 193
  + 839
  ————
  1032

10) 483
  + 662
  ————
  1145

11) 492
  + 860
  ————
  1352

12) 373
  + 863
  ————
  1236

13) 908
  + 318
  ————
  1226

14) 576
  + 246
  ————
   822

15) 392
  + 853
  ————
  1245

16) 496
  + 489
  ————
   985

3 Digit Subtraction No Regrouping

Subtract.

1) 148
  - 102
  ————
    46

2) 126
  - 113
  ————
    13

3) 298
  - 148
  ————
   150

4) 387
  - 343
  ————
    44

5) 149
  - 137
  ————
    12

6) 123
  - 102
  ————
    21

7) 695
  - 253
  ————
   442

8) 798
  - 130
  ————
   668

9) 598
  - 535
  ————
    63

10) 769
  - 554
  ————
   215

11) 464
  - 141
  ————
   323

12) 390
  - 310
  ————
    80

13) 839
  - 316
  ————
   523

14) 452
  - 330
  ————
   122

15) 445
  - 411
  ————
    34

16) 860
  - 230
  ————
   630

3 Digit Subtraction No Regrouping

Subtract.

1) 587
  - 534
  ————
    53

2) 597
  - 120
  ————
   477

3) 133
  - 102
  ————
    31

4) 143
  - 113
  ————
    30

5) 588
  - 453
  ————
   135

6) 564
  - 412
  ————
   152

7) 155
  - 130
  ————
    25

8) 478
  - 201
  ————
   277

9) 515
  - 501
  ————
    14

10) 268
  - 150
  ————
   118

11) 974
  - 502
  ————
   472

12) 746
  - 315
  ————
   431

13) 487
  - 327
  ————
   160

14) 865
  - 202
  ————
   663

15) 878
  - 806
  ————
    72

16) 849
  - 527
  ————
   322

www.claymaze.com

3 Digit Subtraction No Regrouping
Subtract.

1) 959 − 616 = 343
2) 743 − 512 = 231
3) 152 − 102 = 50
4) 794 − 264 = 530

5) 248 − 204 = 44
6) 660 − 440 = 220
7) 777 − 737 = 40
8) 139 − 124 = 15

9) 179 − 160 = 19
10) 734 − 613 = 121
11) 187 − 150 = 37
12) 880 − 220 = 660

13) 898 − 450 = 448
14) 948 − 404 = 544
15) 597 − 362 = 235
16) 469 − 415 = 54

3 Digit Subtraction No Regrouping
Subtract.

1) 969 − 317 = 652
2) 967 − 242 = 725
3) 299 − 262 = 37
4) 366 − 322 = 44

5) 681 − 140 = 541
6) 164 − 152 = 12
7) 576 − 254 = 322
8) 337 − 312 = 25

9) 399 − 114 = 285
10) 949 − 105 = 844
11) 778 − 518 = 260
12) 288 − 214 = 74

13) 921 − 911 = 10
14) 496 − 464 = 32
15) 146 − 133 = 13
16) 766 − 634 = 132

3 Digit Subtraction No Regrouping
Subtract.

1) 954 − 814 = 140
2) 982 − 400 = 582
3) 747 − 727 = 20
4) 160 − 150 = 10

5) 197 − 183 = 14
6) 494 − 300 = 194
7) 242 − 202 = 40
8) 453 − 443 = 10

9) 727 − 700 = 27
10) 349 − 139 = 210
11) 658 − 142 = 516
12) 119 − 103 = 16

13) 273 − 213 = 60
14) 259 − 215 = 44
15) 988 − 764 = 224
16) 521 − 310 = 211

3 Digit Subtraction No Regrouping
Subtract.

1) 197 − 167 = 30
2) 354 − 130 = 224
3) 863 − 732 = 131
4) 128 − 110 = 18

5) 597 − 537 = 60
6) 972 − 260 = 712
7) 189 − 100 = 89
8) 299 − 178 = 121

9) 697 − 453 = 244
10) 947 − 223 = 724
11) 819 − 809 = 10
12) 117 − 107 = 10

13) 888 − 605 = 283
14) 286 − 202 = 84
15) 187 − 121 = 66
16) 878 − 306 = 572

3 Digit Subtraction No Regrouping
Subtract.

1) 393 − 352 = 41
2) 167 − 150 = 17
3) 248 − 132 = 116
4) 758 − 535 = 223

5) 227 − 114 = 113
6) 859 − 502 = 357
7) 549 − 335 = 214
8) 279 − 121 = 158

9) 499 − 327 = 172
10) 596 − 154 = 442
11) 263 − 233 = 30
12) 251 − 130 = 121

13) 631 − 400 = 231
14) 589 − 116 = 473
15) 157 − 112 = 45
16) 757 − 326 = 431

3 Digit Subtraction No Regrouping
Subtract.

1) 391 − 101 = 290
2) 787 − 742 = 45
3) 749 − 112 = 637
4) 596 − 284 = 312

5) 177 − 167 = 10
6) 646 − 135 = 511
7) 896 − 616 = 280
8) 936 − 720 = 216

9) 274 − 252 = 22
10) 986 − 430 = 556
11) 894 − 551 = 343
12) 597 − 232 = 365

13) 979 − 644 = 335
14) 796 − 502 = 294
15) 489 − 412 = 77
16) 726 − 500 = 226

www.claymaze.com

3 Digit Subtraction No Regrouping

Subtract.

1) 956	2) 399	3) 980	4) 988
−636	−344	−410	−558
320	55	570	430

5) 281	6) 134	7) 492	8) 698
−260	−112	−241	−336
21	22	251	362

9) 296	10) 229	11) 878	12) 136
−143	−217	−504	−101
153	12	374	35

13) 285	14) 380	15) 669	16) 293
−162	−270	−334	−240
123	110	335	53

3 Digit Subtraction No Regrouping

Subtract.

1) 188	2) 127	3) 867	4) 645
−147	−105	−241	−211
41	22	626	434

5) 992	6) 126	7) 797	8) 374
−481	−105	−744	−153
511	21	53	221

9) 792	10) 249	11) 174	12) 377
−541	−223	−103	−346
251	26	71	31

13) 584	14) 475	15) 367	16) 274
−274	−451	−331	−263
310	24	36	11

3 Digit Subtraction No Regrouping

Subtract.

1) 878	2) 334	3) 975	4) 786
−707	−320	−552	−654
171	14	423	132

5) 633	6) 267	7) 788	8) 516
−222	−237	−201	−203
411	30	587	313

9) 357	10) 518	11) 699	12) 656
−140	−104	−468	−616
217	414	231	40

13) 287	14) 338	15) 781	16) 196
−244	−217	−570	−102
43	121	211	94

3 Digit Subtraction With Regrouping

Subtract.

1) 262	2) 180	3) 990	4) 791
−239	−126	−233	−768
23	54	757	23

5) 417	6) 828	7) 647	8) 315
−154	−490	−186	−228
263	338	461	87

9) 445	10) 472	11) 221	12) 535
−255	−397	−136	−344
190	75	85	191

13) 845	14) 515	15) 230	16) 872
−479	−167	−171	−513
366	348	59	359

3 Digit Subtraction With Regrouping

Subtract.

1) 712	2) 316	3) 790	4) 784
−259	−235	−552	−487
453	81	238	297

5) 582	6) 271	7) 845	8) 572
−466	−263	−574	−527
116	8	271	45

9) 985	10) 352	11) 807	12) 225
−778	−199	−246	−177
207	153	561	48

13) 248	14) 829	15) 996	16) 430
−171	−651	−599	−358
77	178	397	72

3 Digit Subtraction With Regrouping

Subtract.

1) 565	2) 383	3) 573	4) 920
−183	−247	−188	−274
382	136	385	646

5) 508	6) 191	7) 501	8) 502
−290	−137	−386	−449
218	54	115	53

9) 467	10) 318	11) 686	12) 634
−277	−246	−478	−147
190	72	208	487

13) 923	14) 434	15) 325	16) 253
−497	−384	−262	−172
426	50	63	81

www.claymaze.com

PAGE: 113

3 Digit Subtraction With Regrouping

Subtract.

1) 352 − 338 = 14	2) 964 − 367 = 597	3) 252 − 154 = 98	4) 501 − 205 = 296
5) 528 − 362 = 166	6) 692 − 627 = 65	7) 343 − 148 = 195	8) 727 − 537 = 190
9) 591 − 283 = 308	10) 451 − 389 = 62	11) 571 − 559 = 12	12) 736 − 647 = 89
13) 928 − 387 = 541	14) 203 − 193 = 10	15) 960 − 387 = 573	16) 625 − 386 = 239

PAGE: 114

3 Digit Subtraction With Regrouping

Subtract.

1) 415 − 188 = 227	2) 623 − 561 = 62	3) 170 − 135 = 35	4) 626 − 588 = 38
5) 586 − 348 = 238	6) 426 − 365 = 61	7) 766 − 457 = 309	8) 851 − 423 = 428
9) 520 − 247 = 273	10) 940 − 697 = 243	11) 538 − 378 = 160	12) 653 − 447 = 206
13) 882 − 713 = 169	14) 302 − 115 = 187	15) 611 − 415 = 196	16) 397 − 338 = 59

PAGE: 115

3 Digit Subtraction With Regrouping

Subtract.

1) 120 − 105 = 15	2) 902 − 348 = 554	3) 834 − 746 = 88	4) 723 − 532 = 191
5) 323 − 105 = 218	6) 141 − 108 = 33	7) 687 − 379 = 308	8) 161 − 105 = 56
9) 265 − 179 = 86	10) 278 − 180 = 98	11) 770 − 508 = 262	12) 792 − 409 = 383
13) 164 − 146 = 18	14) 230 − 145 = 85	15) 244 − 117 = 127	16) 492 − 343 = 149

PAGE: 116

3 Digit Subtraction With Regrouping

Subtract.

1) 901 − 821 = 80	2) 920 − 193 = 727	3) 816 − 567 = 249	4) 419 − 294 = 125
5) 693 − 645 = 48	6) 609 − 535 = 74	7) 925 − 139 = 786	8) 791 − 749 = 42
9) 835 − 644 = 191	10) 688 − 339 = 349	11) 903 − 213 = 690	12) 965 − 697 = 268
13) 422 − 288 = 134	14) 304 − 139 = 165	15) 481 − 392 = 89	16) 794 − 196 = 598

PAGE: 117

3 Digit Subtraction With Regrouping

Subtract.

1) 833 − 465 = 368	2) 608 − 161 = 447	3) 326 − 129 = 197	4) 956 − 527 = 429
5) 342 − 117 = 225	6) 670 − 644 = 26	7) 182 − 166 = 16	8) 240 − 152 = 88
9) 337 − 280 = 57	10) 802 − 133 = 669	11) 491 − 458 = 33	12) 944 − 536 = 408
13) 648 − 480 = 168	14) 286 − 119 = 167	15) 365 − 196 = 169	16) 784 − 178 = 606

PAGE: 118

3 Digit Subtraction With Regrouping

Subtract.

1) 739 − 652 = 87	2) 171 − 103 = 68	3) 205 − 125 = 80	4) 303 − 187 = 116
5) 140 − 112 = 28	6) 620 − 403 = 217	7) 975 − 158 = 817	8) 943 − 868 = 75
9) 536 − 271 = 265	10) 858 − 581 = 277	11) 292 − 167 = 125	12) 560 − 375 = 185
13) 214 − 161 = 53	14) 696 − 187 = 509	15) 564 − 157 = 407	16) 809 − 717 = 92

www.claymaze.com

3 Digit Subtraction With Regrouping

Subtract.

1) 729 − 246 = 483	2) 562 − 508 = 54	3) 970 − 583 = 387	4) 830 − 596 = 234
5) 781 − 503 = 278	6) 431 − 207 = 224	7) 541 − 456 = 85	8) 400 − 362 = 38
9) 989 − 697 = 292	10) 306 − 210 = 96	11) 722 − 636 = 86	12) 309 − 289 = 20
13) 706 − 399 = 307	14) 605 − 516 = 89	15) 913 − 233 = 680	16) 941 − 639 = 302

3 Digit Subtraction With Regrouping

Subtract.

1) 625 − 231 = 394	2) 372 − 281 = 91	3) 833 − 537 = 296	4) 922 − 369 = 553
5) 618 − 123 = 495	6) 425 − 157 = 268	7) 707 − 435 = 272	8) 989 − 897 = 92
9) 677 − 378 = 299	10) 646 − 208 = 438	11) 245 − 206 = 39	12) 135 − 128 = 7
13) 691 − 667 = 24	14) 914 − 808 = 106	15) 708 − 410 = 298	16) 161 − 147 = 14

2 Digit Addition Adding 3 Numbers

Add.

1) 59 + 63 + 90 = 212	2) 56 + 11 + 30 = 97	3) 35 + 52 + 11 = 98	4) 61 + 33 + 29 = 123
5) 27 + 57 + 20 = 104	6) 98 + 27 + 37 = 162	7) 10 + 43 + 25 = 78	8) 38 + 29 + 26 = 93
9) 30 + 79 + 65 = 174	10) 41 + 93 + 46 = 180	11) 58 + 43 + 45 = 146	12) 48 + 83 + 28 = 159

2 Digit Addition Adding 3 Numbers

Add.

1) 14 + 54 + 37 = 105	2) 45 + 52 + 14 = 111	3) 35 + 81 + 17 = 133	4) 70 + 60 + 27 = 157
5) 54 + 18 + 54 = 126	6) 15 + 79 + 57 = 151	7) 91 + 43 + 58 = 192	8) 72 + 24 + 62 = 158
9) 87 + 83 + 17 = 187	10) 69 + 42 + 64 = 175	11) 13 + 17 + 19 = 49	12) 86 + 83 + 72 = 241

2 Digit Addition Adding 3 Numbers

Add.

1) 77 + 23 + 76 = 176	2) 95 + 68 + 49 = 212	3) 14 + 28 + 32 = 74	4) 25 + 99 + 43 = 167
5) 34 + 70 + 12 = 116	6) 58 + 94 + 80 = 232	7) 21 + 37 + 95 = 153	8) 86 + 77 + 78 = 241
9) 59 + 75 + 88 = 222	10) 56 + 49 + 77 = 182	11) 67 + 85 + 78 = 230	12) 98 + 77 + 52 = 227

2 Digit Addition Adding 3 Numbers

Add.

1) 37 + 35 + 29 = 101	2) 27 + 13 + 69 = 109	3) 36 + 88 + 11 = 135	4) 17 + 47 + 49 = 113
5) 74 + 67 + 82 = 223	6) 77 + 18 + 92 = 187	7) 25 + 22 + 66 = 113	8) 10 + 77 + 51 = 138
9) 56 + 31 + 14 = 101	10) 58 + 57 + 88 = 203	11) 42 + 67 + 42 = 151	12) 92 + 27 + 94 = 213

www.claymaze.com

2 Digit Addition Adding 3 Numbers

Add.

1) 75 52 +82 209	2) 69 32 +68 169	3) 58 82 +20 160	4) 17 23 +82 122
5) 35 42 +43 120	6) 11 31 +63 105	7) 47 35 +94 176	8) 42 11 +94 147
9) 86 77 +43 206	10) 95 43 +28 166	11) 39 73 +37 149	12) 77 31 +17 125

2 Digit Addition Adding 3 Numbers

Add.

1) 65 81 +59 205	2) 73 15 +65 153	3) 78 30 +88 196	4) 96 96 +72 264
5) 69 58 +54 181	6) 60 57 +60 177	7) 27 81 +14 122	8) 77 48 +88 213
9) 39 40 +12 91	10) 79 95 +12 186	11) 40 94 +11 145	12) 13 27 +41 81

2 Digit Addition Adding 3 Numbers

Add.

1) 20 32 +57 109	2) 44 37 +70 151	3) 37 16 +10 63	4) 31 28 +38 97
5) 82 69 +60 211	6) 63 81 +24 168	7) 29 88 +61 178	8) 51 56 +65 172
9) 79 37 +82 198	10) 43 83 +93 219	11) 89 16 +82 187	12) 85 94 +52 231

2 Digit Addition Adding 3 Numbers

Add.

1) 64 34 +46 144	2) 72 50 +66 188	3) 53 99 +58 210	4) 25 81 +78 184
5) 29 42 +47 118	6) 31 38 +25 94	7) 95 22 +27 144	8) 17 54 +70 141
9) 71 14 +67 152	10) 61 21 +59 141	11) 52 13 +43 108	12) 59 63 +82 204

2 Digit Addition Adding 3 Numbers

Add.

1) 44 40 +71 155	2) 27 91 +37 155	3) 28 98 +30 156	4) 65 85 +52 202
5) 85 43 +80 208	6) 56 72 +25 153	7) 80 51 +33 164	8) 18 14 +22 54
9) 57 77 +36 170	10) 91 94 +29 214	11) 76 64 +52 192	12) 19 61 +63 143

2 Digit Addition Adding 3 Numbers

Add.

1) 68 57 +90 215	2) 52 90 +55 197	3) 56 36 +88 180	4) 38 13 +71 122
5) 82 83 +48 213	6) 31 46 +39 116	7) 25 13 +90 128	8) 73 29 +73 175
9) 98 36 +13 147	10) 37 92 +93 222	11) 65 49 +44 158	12) 96 46 +29 171

www.claymaze.com

2 Digit Addition Adding 3 Numbers

Add.

1)　13
　　84
　+70
　167

2)　85
　　76
　+25
　186

3)　86
　　81
　+62
　229

4)　39
　　31
　+71
　141

5)　60
　　90
　+58
　208

6)　84
　　21
　+97
　202

7)　98
　　19
　+32
　149

8)　22
　　35
　+84
　141

9)　46
　　55
　+69
　170

10)　87
　　60
　+69
　216

11)　58
　　25
　+72
　155

12)　11
　　73
　+30
　114

---

3 Digit Subtraction Regrouping with 0's

Subtract.

1)　300
　−154
　146

2)　900
　−495
　405

3)　400
　−105
　295

4)　400
　−222
　178

5)　400
　−388
　　12

6)　500
　−276
　224

7)　700
　−596
　104

8)　600
　−516
　　84

9)　500
　−202
　298

10)　600
　−447
　153

11)　600
　−336
　264

12)　700
　−479
　221

13)　900
　−649
　251

14)　700
　−319
　381

15)　800
　−357
　443

16)　600
　−156
　444

---

3 Digit Subtraction Regrouping with 0's

Subtract.

1)　400
　−322
　　78

2)　900
　−224
　676

3)　500
　−289
　211

4)　400
　−171
　229

5)　200
　−146
　　54

6)　800
　−351
　449

7)　600
　−175
　425

8)　400
　−324
　　76

9)　900
　−526
　374

10)　600
　−158
　442

11)　400
　−121
　279

12)　700
　−512
　188

13)　700
　−538
　162

14)　300
　−136
　164

15)　300
　−297
　　3

16)　300
　−262
　　38

---

3 Digit Subtraction Regrouping with 0's

Subtract.

1)　200
　−113
　　87

2)　500
　−304
　196

3)　700
　−255
　445

4)　400
　−232
　168

5)　400
　−354
　　46

6)　400
　−322
　　78

7)　700
　−461
　239

8)　800
　−717
　　83

9)　700
　−548
　152

10)　400
　−120
　280

11)　200
　−158
　　42

12)　600
　−373
　227

13)　900
　−262
　638

14)　600
　−472
　128

15)　200
　−109
　　91

16)　500
　−351
　149

---

3 Digit Subtraction Regrouping with 0's

Subtract.

1)　900
　−735
　165

2)　400
　−189
　211

3)　200
　−164
　　36

4)　700
　−615
　　85

5)　600
　−338
　262

6)　700
　−230
　470

7)　700
　−569
　131

8)　700
　−453
　247

9)　400
　−257
　143

10)　300
　−239
　　61

11)　700
　−202
　498

12)　300
　−250
　　50

13)　800
　−583
　217

14)　400
　−243
　157

15)　900
　−541
　359

16)　800
　−162
　638

---

3 Digit Subtraction Regrouping with 0's

Subtract.

1)　800
　−607
　193

2)　700
　−647
　　53

3)　500
　−276
　224

4)　400
　−205
　195

5)　300
　−131
　169

6)　800
　−509
　291

7)　700
　−302
　398

8)　300
　−267
　　33

9)　700
　−672
　　28

10)　900
　−748
　152

11)　600
　−338
　262

12)　400
　−323
　　77

13)　900
　−795
　105

14)　900
　−373
　527

15)　600
　−403
　197

16)　700
　−598
　102

www.claymaze.com

3 Digit Subtraction Regrouping with 0's
Subtract.

1) 400 − 237 = 163
2) 500 − 427 = 73
3) 900 − 413 = 487
4) 200 − 123 = 77
5) 500 − 430 = 70
6) 800 − 748 = 52
7) 900 − 280 = 620
8) 200 − 115 = 85
9) 600 − 381 = 219
10) 300 − 218 = 82
11) 500 − 221 = 279
12) 500 − 296 = 204
13) 600 − 307 = 293
14) 400 − 268 = 132
15) 300 − 174 = 126
16) 900 − 113 = 787

3 Digit Subtraction Regrouping with 0's
Subtract.

1) 800 − 255 = 545
2) 200 − 185 = 15
3) 300 − 220 = 80
4) 400 − 331 = 69
5) 700 − 468 = 232
6) 500 − 481 = 19
7) 900 − 635 = 265
8) 900 − 795 = 105
9) 900 − 602 = 298
10) 900 − 689 = 211
11) 600 − 330 = 270
12) 300 − 155 = 145
13) 400 − 290 = 110
14) 700 − 521 = 179
15) 800 − 182 = 618
16) 200 − 174 = 26

3 Digit Subtraction Regrouping with 0's
Subtract.

1) 600 − 291 = 309
2) 400 − 279 = 121
3) 500 − 257 = 243
4) 300 − 101 = 199
5) 700 − 473 = 227
6) 700 − 202 = 498
7) 300 − 107 = 193
8) 400 − 347 = 53
9) 300 − 121 = 179
10) 400 − 152 = 248
11) 700 − 577 = 123
12) 300 − 290 = 10
13) 900 − 562 = 338
14) 300 − 172 = 128
15) 800 − 395 = 405
16) 700 − 175 = 525

3 Digit Subtraction Regrouping with 0's
Subtract.

1) 400 − 344 = 56
2) 900 − 174 = 726
3) 700 − 256 = 444
4) 300 − 146 = 154
5) 700 − 335 = 365
6) 400 − 205 = 195
7) 800 − 575 = 225
8) 200 − 168 = 32
9) 900 − 171 = 729
10) 400 − 374 = 26
11) 400 − 128 = 272
12) 300 − 159 = 141
13) 700 − 492 = 208
14) 900 − 524 = 376
15) 700 − 247 = 453
16) 200 − 185 = 15

3 Digit Subtraction Regrouping with 0's
Subtract.

1) 800 − 684 = 116
2) 900 − 861 = 39
3) 700 − 635 = 65
4) 600 − 137 = 463
5) 200 − 139 = 61
6) 800 − 749 = 51
7) 400 − 334 = 66
8) 600 − 467 = 133
9) 300 − 110 = 190
10) 600 − 204 = 396
11) 200 − 166 = 34
12) 700 − 444 = 256
13) 800 − 507 = 293
14) 700 − 427 = 273
15) 800 − 298 = 502
16) 700 − 305 = 395

3 Digit Subtraction Regrouping with 0's
Subtract.

1) 800 − 613 = 187
2) 300 − 237 = 63
3) 300 − 180 = 120
4) 400 − 338 = 62
5) 800 − 275 = 525
6) 700 − 328 = 372
7) 200 − 176 = 24
8) 500 − 368 = 132
9) 700 − 630 = 70
10) 200 − 138 = 62
11) 300 − 121 = 179
12) 700 − 537 = 163
13) 300 − 178 = 122
14) 800 − 404 = 396
15) 300 − 140 = 160
16) 700 − 530 = 170

www.claymaze.com

PAGE: 146

Find the Missing Addends

Fill in the blanks.

1) $4 + 5 = 9$
2) $6 + 5 = 11$
3) $6 + 4 = 10$
4) $7 + 6 = 13$
5) $5 + 2 = 7$
6) $4 + 2 = 6$
7) $3 + 8 = 11$
8) $8 + 1 = 9$
9) $6 + 9 = 15$
10) $4 + 3 = 7$
11) $8 + 6 = 14$
12) $7 + 1 = 8$
13) $8 + 2 = 10$
14) $2 + 1 = 3$
15) $3 + 7 = 10$
16) $1 + 1 = 2$
17) $1 + 4 = 5$
18) $5 + 5 = 10$
19) $3 + 3 = 6$
20) $1 + 3 = 4$

PAGE: 147

Find the Missing Addends

Fill in the blanks.

1) $8 + 9 = 17$
2) $2 + 6 = 8$
3) $9 + 4 = 13$
4) $1 + 4 = 5$
5) $6 + 6 = 12$
6) $3 + 4 = 7$
7) $4 + 4 = 8$
8) $6 + 3 = 9$
9) $6 + 8 = 14$
10) $5 + 8 = 13$
11) $9 + 7 = 16$
12) $1 + 1 = 2$
13) $9 + 3 = 12$
14) $4 + 7 = 11$
15) $1 + 7 = 8$
16) $6 + 5 = 11$
17) $1 + 6 = 7$
18) $7 + 2 = 9$
19) $3 + 5 = 8$
20) $6 + 9 = 15$

PAGE: 148

Find the Missing Addends

Fill in the blanks.

1) $4 + 7 = 11$
2) $2 + 6 = 8$
3) $2 + 8 = 10$
4) $6 + 2 = 8$
5) $2 + 1 = 3$
6) $3 + 4 = 7$
7) $6 + 5 = 11$
8) $9 + 8 = 17$
9) $1 + 5 = 6$
10) $8 + 8 = 16$
11) $3 + 3 = 6$
12) $7 + 3 = 10$
13) $5 + 3 = 8$
14) $7 + 9 = 16$
15) $7 + 5 = 12$
16) $4 + 4 = 8$
17) $8 + 9 = 17$
18) $1 + 3 = 4$
19) $8 + 4 = 12$
20) $7 + 4 = 11$

PAGE: 149

Find the Missing Addends

Fill in the blanks.

1) $7 + 1 = 8$
2) $6 + 5 = 11$
3) $6 + 1 = 7$
4) $5 + 1 = 6$
5) $4 + 4 = 8$
6) $2 + 4 = 6$
7) $9 + 9 = 18$
8) $4 + 3 = 7$
9) $7 + 9 = 16$
10) $9 + 2 = 11$
11) $7 + 7 = 14$
12) $4 + 6 = 10$
13) $6 + 6 = 12$
14) $8 + 8 = 16$
15) $9 + 7 = 16$
16) $7 + 6 = 13$
17) $8 + 9 = 17$
18) $8 + 2 = 10$
19) $9 + 3 = 12$
20) $9 + 1 = 10$

PAGE: 150

Find the Missing Addends

Fill in the blanks.

1) $5 + 4 = 9$
2) $8 + 5 = 13$
3) $9 + 1 = 10$
4) $2 + 4 = 6$
5) $6 + 8 = 14$
6) $8 + 7 = 15$
7) $1 + 4 = 5$
8) $1 + 5 = 6$
9) $4 + 7 = 11$
10) $3 + 6 = 9$
11) $5 + 2 = 7$
12) $9 + 4 = 13$
13) $9 + 8 = 17$
14) $6 + 6 = 12$
15) $8 + 1 = 9$
16) $7 + 8 = 15$
17) $4 + 2 = 6$
18) $3 + 5 = 8$
19) $7 + 5 = 12$
20) $5 + 7 = 12$

PAGE: 151

Find the Missing Addends

Fill in the blanks.

1) $6 + 5 = 11$
2) $4 + 2 = 6$
3) $6 + 9 = 15$
4) $3 + 3 = 6$
5) $7 + 4 = 11$
6) $9 + 9 = 18$
7) $5 + 8 = 13$
8) $3 + 8 = 11$
9) $8 + 9 = 17$
10) $4 + 7 = 11$
11) $3 + 7 = 10$
12) $2 + 2 = 4$
13) $6 + 7 = 13$
14) $2 + 8 = 10$
15) $1 + 4 = 5$
16) $2 + 5 = 7$
17) $6 + 3 = 9$
18) $1 + 8 = 9$
19) $7 + 3 = 10$
20) $4 + 5 = 9$

www.claymaze.com

PAGE: 152

Find the Missing Addends

Fill in the blanks.

1) $3 + \underline{1} = 4$ 11) $8 + \underline{5} = 13$

2) $1 + \underline{7} = 8$ 12) $9 + \underline{2} = 11$

3) $1 + \underline{5} = 6$ 13) $5 + \underline{8} = 13$

4) $8 + \underline{7} = 15$ 14) $2 + \underline{6} = 8$

5) $7 + \underline{3} = 10$ 15) $8 + \underline{3} = 11$

6) $4 + \underline{4} = 8$ 16) $9 + \underline{8} = 17$

7) $1 + \underline{2} = 3$ 17) $5 + \underline{6} = 11$

8) $9 + \underline{4} = 13$ 18) $8 + \underline{8} = 16$

9) $3 + \underline{2} = 5$ 19) $8 + \underline{9} = 17$

10) $8 + \underline{1} = 9$ 20) $9 + \underline{1} = 10$

PAGE: 153

Find the Missing Addends

Fill in the blanks.

1) $3 + \underline{3} = 6$ 11) $7 + \underline{8} = 15$

2) $7 + \underline{6} = 13$ 12) $3 + \underline{2} = 5$

3) $6 + \underline{4} = 10$ 13) $9 + \underline{1} = 10$

4) $3 + \underline{4} = 7$ 14) $8 + \underline{3} = 11$

5) $4 + \underline{9} = 13$ 15) $5 + \underline{8} = 13$

6) $3 + \underline{8} = 11$ 16) $6 + \underline{2} = 8$

7) $5 + \underline{6} = 11$ 17) $9 + \underline{6} = 15$

8) $5 + \underline{9} = 14$ 18) $3 + \underline{6} = 9$

9) $7 + \underline{3} = 10$ 19) $2 + \underline{4} = 6$

10) $5 + \underline{4} = 9$ 20) $7 + \underline{7} = 14$

PAGE: 154

Find the Missing Addends

Fill in the blanks.

1) $8 + \underline{7} = 15$ 11) $4 + \underline{9} = 13$

2) $2 + \underline{1} = 3$ 12) $3 + \underline{6} = 9$

3) $8 + \underline{5} = 13$ 13) $6 + \underline{3} = 9$

4) $8 + \underline{6} = 14$ 14) $1 + \underline{6} = 7$

5) $7 + \underline{4} = 11$ 15) $9 + \underline{3} = 12$

6) $4 + \underline{6} = 10$ 16) $9 + \underline{6} = 15$

7) $4 + \underline{3} = 7$ 17) $6 + \underline{9} = 15$

8) $6 + \underline{7} = 13$ 18) $3 + \underline{9} = 12$

9) $3 + \underline{3} = 6$ 19) $7 + \underline{2} = 9$

10) $9 + \underline{4} = 13$ 20) $5 + \underline{1} = 6$

PAGE: 155

Find the Missing Addends

Fill in the blanks.

1) $4 + \underline{6} = 10$ 11) $4 + \underline{9} = 13$

2) $5 + \underline{9} = 14$ 12) $2 + \underline{4} = 6$

3) $6 + \underline{5} = 11$ 13) $9 + \underline{1} = 10$

4) $7 + \underline{8} = 15$ 14) $5 + \underline{5} = 10$

5) $3 + \underline{1} = 4$ 15) $2 + \underline{3} = 5$

6) $3 + \underline{8} = 11$ 16) $2 + \underline{1} = 3$

7) $8 + \underline{4} = 12$ 17) $9 + \underline{5} = 14$

8) $8 + \underline{7} = 15$ 18) $1 + \underline{2} = 3$

9) $6 + \underline{1} = 7$ 19) $4 + \underline{7} = 11$

10) $2 + \underline{5} = 7$ 20) $6 + \underline{2} = 8$

PAGE: 156

Find the Missing Addends

Fill in the blanks.

1) $4 + \underline{9} = 13$ 11) $6 + \underline{2} = 8$

2) $3 + \underline{9} = 12$ 12) $7 + \underline{8} = 15$

3) $8 + \underline{1} = 9$ 13) $1 + \underline{7} = 8$

4) $9 + \underline{8} = 17$ 14) $1 + \underline{8} = 9$

5) $7 + \underline{9} = 16$ 15) $5 + \underline{1} = 6$

6) $8 + \underline{4} = 12$ 16) $3 + \underline{8} = 11$

7) $1 + \underline{9} = 10$ 17) $5 + \underline{2} = 7$

8) $8 + \underline{3} = 11$ 18) $4 + \underline{8} = 12$

9) $8 + \underline{7} = 15$ 19) $2 + \underline{9} = 11$

10) $8 + \underline{9} = 17$ 20) $9 + \underline{1} = 10$

PAGE: 158

Find the Missing Addends

Fill in the blanks.

1) $70 + \underline{40} = 110$ 11) $70 + \underline{80} = 150$

2) $10 + \underline{90} = 100$ 12) $10 + \underline{80} = 90$

3) $80 + \underline{60} = 140$ 13) $10 + \underline{50} = 60$

4) $20 + \underline{60} = 80$ 14) $40 + \underline{20} = 60$

5) $70 + \underline{50} = 120$ 15) $30 + \underline{30} = 60$

6) $20 + \underline{70} = 90$ 16) $10 + \underline{60} = 70$

7) $50 + \underline{60} = 110$ 17) $40 + \underline{90} = 130$

8) $60 + \underline{90} = 150$ 18) $30 + \underline{70} = 100$

9) $80 + \underline{20} = 100$ 19) $30 + \underline{90} = 120$

10) $20 + \underline{50} = 70$ 20) $60 + \underline{50} = 110$

PAGE: 159

Find the Missing Addends

Fill in the blanks.

1) 60 + _70_ = 130
2) 50 + _20_ = 70
3) 10 + _40_ = 50
4) 70 + _70_ = 140
5) 50 + _60_ = 110
6) 70 + _20_ = 90
7) 50 + _10_ = 60
8) 20 + _40_ = 60
9) 90 + _30_ = 120
10) 60 + _80_ = 140

11) 10 + _60_ = 70
12) 30 + _40_ = 70
13) 90 + _10_ = 100
14) 30 + _30_ = 60
15) 80 + _50_ = 130
16) 10 + _50_ = 60
17) 60 + _60_ = 120
18) 80 + _60_ = 140
19) 80 + _80_ = 160
20) 30 + _80_ = 110

PAGE: 160

Find the Missing Addends

Fill in the blanks.

1) 70 + _10_ = 80
2) 80 + _20_ = 100
3) 30 + _40_ = 70
4) 10 + _40_ = 50
5) 20 + _90_ = 110
6) 50 + _20_ = 70
7) 80 + _80_ = 160
8) 60 + _40_ = 100
9) 80 + _60_ = 140
10) 80 + _40_ = 120

11) 40 + _40_ = 80
12) 10 + _10_ = 20
13) 70 + _20_ = 90
14) 50 + _50_ = 100
15) 90 + _40_ = 130
16) 80 + _90_ = 170
17) 40 + _60_ = 100
18) 90 + _70_ = 160
19) 60 + _90_ = 150
20) 70 + _50_ = 120

PAGE: 161

Find the Missing Addends

Fill in the blanks.

1) 20 + _70_ = 90
2) 60 + _70_ = 130
3) 30 + _20_ = 50
4) 40 + _50_ = 90
5) 90 + _50_ = 140
6) 20 + _80_ = 100
7) 10 + _50_ = 60
8) 70 + _50_ = 120
9) 30 + _60_ = 90
10) 90 + _80_ = 170

11) 90 + _70_ = 160
12) 30 + _50_ = 80
13) 20 + _40_ = 60
14) 90 + _60_ = 150
15) 90 + _10_ = 100
16) 50 + _70_ = 120
17) 70 + _80_ = 150
18) 60 + _90_ = 150
19) 10 + _30_ = 40
20) 80 + _20_ = 100

PAGE: 162

Find the Missing Addends

Fill in the blanks.

1) 80 + _10_ = 90
2) 60 + _50_ = 110
3) 60 + _30_ = 90
4) 20 + _30_ = 50
5) 50 + _10_ = 60
6) 10 + _60_ = 70
7) 90 + _60_ = 150
8) 80 + _80_ = 160
9) 80 + _50_ = 130
10) 50 + _30_ = 80

11) 30 + _70_ = 100
12) 60 + _60_ = 120
13) 70 + _20_ = 90
14) 20 + _10_ = 30
15) 40 + _20_ = 60
16) 10 + _40_ = 50
17) 40 + _40_ = 80
18) 90 + _90_ = 180
19) 80 + _70_ = 150
20) 20 + _50_ = 70

PAGE: 163

Find the Missing Addends

Fill in the blanks.

1) 90 + _50_ = 140
2) 60 + _80_ = 140
3) 80 + _50_ = 130
4) 10 + _20_ = 30
5) 40 + _10_ = 50
6) 50 + _10_ = 60
7) 40 + _20_ = 60
8) 70 + _20_ = 90
9) 60 + _40_ = 100
10) 50 + _50_ = 100

11) 90 + _90_ = 180
12) 40 + _80_ = 120
13) 30 + _80_ = 110
14) 20 + _60_ = 80
15) 80 + _10_ = 90
16) 50 + _60_ = 110
17) 20 + _40_ = 60
18) 10 + _70_ = 80
19) 10 + _50_ = 60
20) 60 + _50_ = 110

PAGE: 164

Find the Missing Addends

Fill in the blanks.

1) 60 + _60_ = 120
2) 50 + _50_ = 100
3) 30 + _40_ = 70
4) 60 + _10_ = 70
5) 40 + _70_ = 110
6) 40 + _10_ = 50
7) 60 + _20_ = 80
8) 70 + _90_ = 160
9) 70 + _60_ = 130
10) 90 + _90_ = 180

11) 40 + _40_ = 80
12) 70 + _70_ = 140
13) 70 + _50_ = 120
14) 40 + _30_ = 70
15) 80 + _80_ = 160
16) 30 + _70_ = 100
17) 60 + _90_ = 150
18) 20 + _90_ = 110
19) 50 + _60_ = 110
20) 90 + _10_ = 100

Find the Missing Addends

Fill in the blanks.

1) $70 + \underline{70} = 140$ 11) $70 + \underline{20} = 90$

2) $90 + \underline{20} = 110$ 12) $40 + \underline{70} = 110$

3) $90 + \underline{70} = 160$ 13) $10 + \underline{80} = 90$

4) $60 + \underline{30} = 90$ 14) $40 + \underline{40} = 80$

5) $20 + \underline{40} = 60$ 15) $30 + \underline{50} = 80$

6) $50 + \underline{10} = 60$ 16) $50 + \underline{80} = 130$

7) $10 + \underline{60} = 70$ 17) $20 + \underline{70} = 90$

8) $50 + \underline{20} = 70$ 18) $70 + \underline{80} = 150$

9) $40 + \underline{10} = 50$ 19) $50 + \underline{50} = 100$

10) $80 + \underline{30} = 110$ 20) $90 + \underline{50} = 140$

Find the Missing Addends

Fill in the blanks.

1) $80 + \underline{40} = 120$ 11) $80 + \underline{50} = 130$

2) $30 + \underline{60} = 90$ 12) $50 + \underline{70} = 120$

3) $20 + \underline{20} = 40$ 13) $60 + \underline{20} = 80$

4) $20 + \underline{80} = 100$ 14) $70 + \underline{40} = 110$

5) $20 + \underline{70} = 90$ 15) $50 + \underline{30} = 80$

6) $90 + \underline{60} = 150$ 16) $40 + \underline{30} = 70$

7) $50 + \underline{60} = 110$ 17) $30 + \underline{50} = 80$

8) $30 + \underline{20} = 50$ 18) $10 + \underline{70} = 80$

9) $50 + \underline{50} = 100$ 19) $70 + \underline{70} = 140$

10) $50 + \underline{80} = 130$ 20) $80 + \underline{90} = 170$

Find the Missing Addends

Fill in the blanks.

1) $50 + \underline{60} = 110$ 11) $80 + \underline{30} = 110$

2) $50 + \underline{20} = 70$ 12) $80 + \underline{40} = 120$

3) $10 + \underline{70} = 80$ 13) $40 + \underline{40} = 80$

4) $70 + \underline{90} = 160$ 14) $60 + \underline{10} = 70$

5) $60 + \underline{40} = 100$ 15) $40 + \underline{80} = 120$

6) $30 + \underline{90} = 120$ 16) $20 + \underline{30} = 50$

7) $10 + \underline{10} = 20$ 17) $30 + \underline{50} = 80$

8) $30 + \underline{30} = 60$ 18) $40 + \underline{60} = 100$

9) $80 + \underline{60} = 140$ 19) $10 + \underline{30} = 40$

10) $20 + \underline{20} = 40$ 20) $50 + \underline{70} = 120$

Find the Missing Addends

Fill in the blanks.

1) $70 + \underline{80} = 150$ 11) $20 + \underline{70} = 90$

2) $30 + \underline{80} = 110$ 12) $10 + \underline{10} = 20$

3) $10 + \underline{80} = 90$ 13) $40 + \underline{80} = 120$

4) $70 + \underline{90} = 160$ 14) $70 + \underline{20} = 90$

5) $10 + \underline{50} = 60$ 15) $90 + \underline{90} = 180$

6) $10 + \underline{20} = 30$ 16) $70 + \underline{50} = 120$

7) $80 + \underline{30} = 110$ 17) $80 + \underline{90} = 170$

8) $90 + \underline{40} = 130$ 18) $60 + \underline{60} = 120$

9) $50 + \underline{90} = 140$ 19) $90 + \underline{50} = 140$

10) $20 + \underline{50} = 70$ 20) $30 + \underline{20} = 50$

Find the Missing Addends

Fill in the blanks.

1) $83 + \underline{6} = 89$ 11) $\underline{70} + 6 = 76$

2) $\underline{57} + 2 = 59$ 12) $54 + \underline{2} = 56$

3) $67 + \underline{1} = 68$ 13) $\underline{78} + 1 = 79$

4) $\underline{22} + 6 = 28$ 14) $29 + \underline{1} = 30$

5) $51 + \underline{3} = 54$ 15) $\underline{14} + 4 = 18$

6) $\underline{63} + 2 = 65$ 16) $98 + \underline{1} = 99$

7) $12 + \underline{4} = 16$ 17) $\underline{32} + 3 = 35$

8) $\underline{71} + 8 = 79$ 18) $60 + \underline{4} = 64$

9) $16 + \underline{2} = 18$ 19) $\underline{18} + 1 = 19$

10) $\underline{64} + 4 = 68$ 20) $92 + \underline{3} = 95$

Find the Missing Addends

Fill in the blanks.

1) $95 + \underline{1} = 96$ 11) $\underline{66} + 3 = 69$

2) $\underline{58} + 1 = 59$ 12) $93 + \underline{1} = 94$

3) $36 + \underline{3} = 39$ 13) $\underline{17} + 1 = 18$

4) $\underline{49} + 1 = 50$ 14) $12 + \underline{5} = 17$

5) $72 + \underline{3} = 75$ 15) $\underline{33} + 4 = 37$

6) $\underline{34} + 3 = 37$ 16) $76 + \underline{2} = 78$

7) $90 + \underline{5} = 95$ 17) $\underline{53} + 5 = 58$

8) $\underline{41} + 7 = 48$ 18) $68 + \underline{1} = 69$

9) $86 + \underline{3} = 89$ 19) $\underline{74} + 1 = 75$

10) $\underline{11} + 7 = 18$ 20) $23 + \underline{5} = 28$

---

www.claymaze.com

Find the Missing Addends

Fill in the blanks.

1) $51 + 8 = 59$
2) $26 + 3 = 29$
3) $21 + 3 = 24$
4) $57 + 2 = 59$
5) $15 + 1 = 16$
6) $47 + 2 = 49$
7) $96 + 2 = 98$
8) $78 + 1 = 79$
9) $34 + 4 = 38$
10) $56 + 1 = 57$
11) $11 + 2 = 13$
12) $85 + 4 = 89$
13) $18 + 1 = 19$
14) $72 + 7 = 79$
15) $22 + 1 = 23$
16) $20 + 7 = 27$
17) $55 + 2 = 57$
18) $94 + 1 = 95$
19) $67 + 1 = 68$
20) $90 + 8 = 98$

Find the Missing Addends

Fill in the blanks.

1) $46 + 3 = 49$
2) $25 + 3 = 28$
3) $70 + 8 = 78$
4) $81 + 2 = 83$
5) $42 + 1 = 43$
6) $29 + 1 = 30$
7) $53 + 5 = 58$
8) $26 + 3 = 29$
9) $62 + 1 = 63$
10) $95 + 1 = 96$
11) $34 + 3 = 37$
12) $66 + 3 = 69$
13) $58 + 1 = 59$
14) $39 + 1 = 40$
15) $89 + 1 = 90$
16) $17 + 2 = 19$
17) $37 + 1 = 38$
18) $69 + 1 = 70$
19) $55 + 3 = 58$
20) $67 + 2 = 69$

Find the Missing Addends

Fill in the blanks.

1) $36 + 2 = 38$
2) $60 + 7 = 67$
3) $31 + 2 = 33$
4) $34 + 1 = 35$
5) $20 + 9 = 29$
6) $92 + 6 = 98$
7) $33 + 5 = 38$
8) $66 + 2 = 68$
9) $23 + 5 = 28$
10) $80 + 5 = 85$
11) $37 + 1 = 38$
12) $26 + 3 = 29$
13) $56 + 2 = 58$
14) $83 + 2 = 85$
15) $52 + 7 = 59$
16) $87 + 2 = 89$
17) $19 + 1 = 20$
18) $14 + 3 = 17$
19) $93 + 6 = 99$
20) $35 + 3 = 38$

Find the Missing Addends

Fill in the blanks.

1) $41 + 3 = 44$
2) $27 + 2 = 29$
3) $23 + 6 = 29$
4) $60 + 1 = 61$
5) $35 + 1 = 36$
6) $68 + 1 = 69$
7) $55 + 3 = 58$
8) $76 + 3 = 79$
9) $94 + 3 = 97$
10) $28 + 1 = 29$
11) $13 + 3 = 16$
12) $36 + 1 = 37$
13) $69 + 1 = 70$
14) $29 + 1 = 30$
15) $59 + 1 = 60$
16) $79 + 1 = 80$
17) $52 + 4 = 56$
18) $40 + 2 = 42$
19) $86 + 2 = 88$
20) $45 + 1 = 46$

Find the Missing Addends

Fill in the blanks.

1) $67 + 1 = 68$
2) $71 + 2 = 73$
3) $81 + 5 = 86$
4) $60 + 9 = 69$
5) $18 + 1 = 19$
6) $96 + 3 = 99$
7) $36 + 3 = 39$
8) $38 + 1 = 39$
9) $89 + 1 = 90$
10) $20 + 4 = 24$
11) $41 + 3 = 44$
12) $22 + 3 = 25$
13) $19 + 1 = 20$
14) $61 + 2 = 63$
15) $48 + 1 = 49$
16) $97 + 2 = 99$
17) $49 + 1 = 50$
18) $83 + 1 = 84$
19) $50 + 6 = 56$
20) $28 + 1 = 29$

Find the Missing Addends

Fill in the blanks.

1) $51 + 7 = 58$
2) $46 + 3 = 49$
3) $90 + 8 = 98$
4) $49 + 1 = 50$
5) $96 + 1 = 97$
6) $95 + 1 = 96$
7) $44 + 2 = 46$
8) $74 + 2 = 76$
9) $92 + 4 = 96$
10) $84 + 3 = 87$
11) $89 + 1 = 90$
12) $72 + 5 = 77$
13) $43 + 2 = 45$
14) $21 + 1 = 22$
15) $70 + 6 = 76$
16) $30 + 7 = 37$
17) $56 + 2 = 58$
18) $78 + 1 = 79$
19) $73 + 3 = 76$
20) $23 + 2 = 25$

www.claymaze.com

Find the Missing Addends

Fill in the blanks.

1) $15 + \underline{4} = 19$
2) $\underline{30} + 2 = 32$
3) $92 + \underline{7} = 99$
4) $\underline{33} + 3 = 36$
5) $82 + \underline{4} = 86$
6) $\underline{71} + 2 = 73$
7) $52 + \underline{3} = 55$
8) $\underline{34} + 1 = 35$
9) $69 + \underline{1} = 70$
10) $\underline{76} + 3 = 79$

11) $\underline{81} + 8 = 89$
12) $55 + \underline{2} = 57$
13) $\underline{63} + 6 = 69$
14) $94 + \underline{4} = 98$
15) $\underline{87} + 1 = 88$
16) $29 + \underline{1} = 30$
17) $\underline{40} + 4 = 44$
18) $17 + \underline{2} = 19$
19) $\underline{79} + 1 = 80$
20) $66 + \underline{1} = 67$

Find the Missing Addends

Fill in the blanks.

1) $11 + \underline{8} = 19$
2) $\underline{58} + 1 = 59$
3) $37 + \underline{2} = 39$
4) $\underline{70} + 5 = 75$
5) $40 + \underline{3} = 43$
6) $\underline{43} + 5 = 48$
7) $20 + \underline{7} = 27$
8) $\underline{47} + 2 = 49$
9) $64 + \underline{3} = 67$
10) $\underline{79} + 1 = 80$

11) $\underline{85} + 4 = 89$
12) $98 + \underline{1} = 99$
13) $\underline{46} + 2 = 48$
14) $87 + \underline{2} = 89$
15) $\underline{17} + 2 = 19$
16) $67 + \underline{2} = 69$
17) $\underline{68} + 1 = 69$
18) $72 + \underline{7} = 79$
19) $\underline{55} + 3 = 58$
20) $60 + \underline{7} = 67$

Find the Missing Addends

Fill in the blanks.

1) $54 + \underline{4} = 58$
2) $\underline{65} + 2 = 67$
3) $33 + \underline{1} = 34$
4) $\underline{98} + 1 = 99$
5) $92 + \underline{3} = 95$
6) $\underline{67} + 2 = 69$
7) $31 + \underline{3} = 34$
8) $\underline{38} + 1 = 39$
9) $95 + \underline{4} = 99$
10) $\underline{77} + 2 = 79$

11) $\underline{55} + 3 = 58$
12) $74 + \underline{5} = 79$
13) $\underline{14} + 5 = 19$
14) $85 + \underline{4} = 89$
15) $\underline{93} + 5 = 98$
16) $70 + \underline{3} = 73$
17) $\underline{90} + 1 = 91$
18) $96 + \underline{3} = 99$
19) $\underline{73} + 4 = 77$
20) $52 + \underline{4} = 56$

Find the Missing Subtrahends

Fill in the blanks.

1) $5 - \underline{2} = 3$
2) $10 - \underline{3} = 7$
3) $2 - \underline{2} = 0$
4) $10 - \underline{1} = 9$
5) $15 - \underline{9} = 6$
6) $13 - \underline{4} = 9$
7) $7 - \underline{6} = 1$
8) $8 - \underline{2} = 6$
9) $4 - \underline{4} = 0$
10) $8 - \underline{1} = 7$

11) $17 - \underline{8} = 9$
12) $18 - \underline{9} = 9$
13) $11 - \underline{6} = 5$
14) $16 - \underline{7} = 9$
15) $3 - \underline{1} = 2$
16) $16 - \underline{8} = 8$
17) $4 - \underline{2} = 2$
18) $15 - \underline{8} = 7$
19) $6 - \underline{5} = 1$
20) $7 - \underline{4} = 3$

Find the Missing Subtrahends

Fill in the blanks.

1) $2 - \underline{2} = 0$
2) $8 - \underline{6} = 2$
3) $15 - \underline{9} = 6$
4) $10 - \underline{9} = 1$
5) $16 - \underline{7} = 9$
6) $3 - \underline{2} = 1$
7) $11 - \underline{6} = 5$
8) $4 - \underline{1} = 3$
9) $6 - \underline{4} = 2$
10) $7 - \underline{1} = 6$

11) $6 - \underline{5} = 1$
12) $4 - \underline{2} = 2$
13) $14 - \underline{6} = 8$
14) $17 - \underline{8} = 9$
15) $18 - \underline{9} = 9$
16) $11 - \underline{2} = 9$
17) $6 - \underline{3} = 3$
18) $13 - \underline{4} = 9$
19) $14 - \underline{9} = 5$
20) $12 - \underline{4} = 8$

Find the Missing Subtrahends

Fill in the blanks.

1) $18 - \underline{9} = 9$
2) $4 - \underline{1} = 3$
3) $8 - \underline{7} = 1$
4) $8 - \underline{2} = 6$
5) $5 - \underline{3} = 2$
6) $10 - \underline{5} = 5$
7) $10 - \underline{2} = 8$
8) $13 - \underline{5} = 8$
9) $6 - \underline{4} = 2$
10) $2 - \underline{2} = 0$

11) $15 - \underline{8} = 7$
12) $11 - \underline{7} = 4$
13) $9 - \underline{8} = 1$
14) $14 - \underline{7} = 7$
15) $2 - \underline{1} = 1$
16) $14 - \underline{9} = 5$
17) $14 - \underline{8} = 6$
18) $6 - \underline{2} = 4$
19) $11 - \underline{5} = 6$
20) $13 - \underline{4} = 9$

www.claymaze.com

Find the Missing Subtrahends

Fill in the blanks.

1) 14 - 7 = 7
2) 3 - 3 = 0
3) 7 - 7 = 0
4) 17 - 9 = 8
5) 13 - 8 = 5
6) 15 - 9 = 6
7) 2 - 1 = 1
8) 6 - 4 = 2
9) 12 - 8 = 4
10) 14 - 6 = 8

11) 15 - 7 = 8
12) 3 - 1 = 2
13) 9 - 2 = 7
14) 16 - 8 = 8
15) 18 - 9 = 9
16) 13 - 5 = 8
17) 12 - 4 = 8
18) 7 - 1 = 6
19) 11 - 8 = 3
20) 8 - 3 = 5

Find the Missing Subtrahends

Fill in the blanks.

1) 18 - 9 = 9
2) 7 - 7 = 0
3) 17 - 9 = 8
4) 6 - 3 = 3
5) 9 - 1 = 8
6) 4 - 2 = 2
7) 9 - 7 = 2
8) 16 - 9 = 7
9) 11 - 6 = 5
10) 3 - 1 = 2

11) 7 - 3 = 4
12) 14 - 7 = 7
13) 9 - 5 = 4
14) 16 - 7 = 9
15) 13 - 4 = 9
16) 8 - 8 = 0
17) 14 - 8 = 6
18) 4 - 4 = 0
19) 8 - 3 = 5
20) 16 - 8 = 8

Find the Missing Subtrahends

Fill in the blanks.

1) 11 - 4 = 7
2) 11 - 3 = 8
3) 5 - 4 = 1
4) 3 - 3 = 0
5) 7 - 5 = 2
6) 6 - 2 = 4
7) 15 - 6 = 9
8) 11 - 7 = 4
9) 6 - 5 = 1
10) 7 - 6 = 1

11) 8 - 4 = 4
12) 6 - 4 = 2
13) 9 - 9 = 0
14) 4 - 4 = 0
15) 8 - 7 = 1
16) 9 - 7 = 2
17) 7 - 3 = 4
18) 12 - 4 = 8
19) 8 - 2 = 6
20) 10 - 5 = 5

Find the Missing Subtrahends

Fill in the blanks.

1) 6 - 3 = 3
2) 16 - 8 = 8
3) 17 - 9 = 8
4) 14 - 5 = 9
5) 7 - 3 = 4
6) 10 - 4 = 6
7) 14 - 9 = 5
8) 17 - 8 = 9
9) 12 - 8 = 4
10) 4 - 1 = 3

11) 15 - 8 = 7
12) 13 - 4 = 9
13) 3 - 2 = 1
14) 2 - 2 = 0
15) 4 - 3 = 1
16) 7 - 6 = 1
17) 18 - 9 = 9
18) 13 - 8 = 5
19) 15 - 7 = 8
20) 8 - 2 = 6

Find the Missing Subtrahends

Fill in the blanks.

1) 7 - 1 = 6
2) 12 - 4 = 8
3) 15 - 6 = 9
4) 14 - 7 = 7
5) 14 - 6 = 8
6) 13 - 9 = 4
7) 17 - 8 = 9
8) 13 - 7 = 6
9) 12 - 5 = 7
10) 7 - 6 = 1

11) 7 - 5 = 2
12) 8 - 8 = 0
13) 11 - 5 = 6
14) 9 - 9 = 0
15) 4 - 3 = 1
16) 7 - 2 = 5
17) 5 - 2 = 3
18) 2 - 1 = 1
19) 3 - 1 = 2
20) 16 - 8 = 8

Find the Missing Subtrahends

Fill in the blanks.

1) 9 - 6 = 3
2) 6 - 1 = 5
3) 16 - 8 = 8
4) 14 - 5 = 9
5) 4 - 4 = 0
6) 13 - 5 = 8
7) 13 - 8 = 5
8) 17 - 8 = 9
9) 6 - 2 = 4
10) 11 - 5 = 6

11) 7 - 6 = 1
12) 9 - 7 = 2
13) 12 - 8 = 4
14) 3 - 3 = 0
15) 9 - 4 = 5
16) 16 - 9 = 7
17) 9 - 5 = 4
18) 4 - 2 = 2
19) 17 - 9 = 8
20) 6 - 5 = 1

www.claymaze.com

Find the Missing Subtrahends

Fill in the blanks.

1) 13 - 4 = 9
2) 12 - 4 = 8
3) 6 - 6 = 0
4) 3 - 2 = 1
5) 17 - 8 = 9
6) 3 - 1 = 2
7) 9 - 5 = 4
8) 6 - 5 = 1
9) 10 - 7 = 3
10) 9 - 1 = 8
11) 10 - 5 = 5
12) 6 - 2 = 4
13) 7 - 1 = 6
14) 15 - 8 = 7
15) 5 - 2 = 3
16) 13 - 6 = 7
17) 16 - 9 = 7
18) 14 - 7 = 7
19) 18 - 9 = 9
20) 17 - 9 = 8

Find the Missing Subtrahends

Fill in the blanks.

1) 17 - 8 = 9
2) 11 - 8 = 3
3) 12 - 7 = 5
4) 14 - 8 = 6
5) 9 - 7 = 2
6) 7 - 3 = 4
7) 4 - 3 = 1
8) 10 - 1 = 9
9) 15 - 8 = 7
10) 16 - 9 = 7
11) 4 - 1 = 3
12) 18 - 9 = 9
13) 13 - 8 = 5
14) 7 - 6 = 1
15) 12 - 8 = 4
16) 9 - 9 = 0
17) 8 - 1 = 7
18) 7 - 1 = 6
19) 16 - 8 = 8
20) 12 - 4 = 8

Find the Missing Subtrahends

Fill in the blanks.

1) 130 - 80 = 50
2) 90 - 10 = 80
3) 110 - 80 = 30
4) 60 - 50 = 10
5) 50 - 20 = 30
6) 80 - 40 = 40
7) 150 - 70 = 80
8) 90 - 30 = 60
9) 60 - 40 = 20
10) 170 - 90 = 80
11) 90 - 30 = 60
12) 140 - 90 = 50
13) 120 - 70 = 50
14) 160 - 80 = 80
15) 110 - 40 = 70
16) 70 - 30 = 40
17) 180 - 90 = 90
18) 170 - 80 = 90
19) 150 - 70 = 80
20) 50 - 20 = 30

Find the Missing Subtrahends

Fill in the blanks.

1) 150 - 60 = 90
2) 70 - 50 = 20
3) 130 - 90 = 40
4) 90 - 70 = 20
5) 90 - 30 = 60
6) 80 - 60 = 20
7) 160 - 90 = 70
8) 50 - 40 = 10
9) 60 - 50 = 10
10) 150 - 90 = 60
11) 90 - 20 = 70
12) 130 - 50 = 80
13) 140 - 90 = 50
14) 100 - 80 = 20
15) 130 - 80 = 50
16) 80 - 10 = 70
17) 130 - 70 = 60
18) 150 - 80 = 70
19) 110 - 80 = 30
20) 90 - 60 = 30

Find the Missing Subtrahends

Fill in the blanks.

1) 110 - 50 = 60
2) 50 - 40 = 10
3) 100 - 40 = 60
4) 70 - 50 = 20
5) 120 - 70 = 50
6) 70 - 40 = 30
7) 120 - 80 = 40
8) 50 - 30 = 20
9) 80 - 70 = 10
10) 90 - 80 = 10
11) 150 - 60 = 90
12) 110 - 90 = 20
13) 130 - 90 = 40
14) 80 - 60 = 20
15) 90 - 20 = 70
16) 30 - 10 = 20
17) 70 - 20 = 50
18) 130 - 50 = 80
19) 100 - 10 = 90
20) 20 - 10 = 10

Find the Missing Subtrahends

Fill in the blanks.

1) 140 - 80 = 60
2) 130 - 70 = 60
3) 110 - 20 = 90
4) 100 - 60 = 40
5) 140 - 70 = 70
6) 170 - 90 = 80
7) 40 - 10 = 30
8) 80 - 70 = 10
9) 110 - 30 = 80
10) 50 - 10 = 40
11) 20 - 10 = 10
12) 160 - 90 = 70
13) 60 - 10 = 50
14) 60 - 50 = 10
15) 160 - 80 = 80
16) 90 - 10 = 80
17) 80 - 50 = 30
18) 90 - 50 = 40
19) 170 - 80 = 90
20) 100 - 30 = 70

Find the Missing Subtrahends

Fill in the blanks.

1) 100 - _40_ = 60
2) 20 - _10_ = 10
3) 110 - _20_ = 90
4) 140 - _60_ = 80
5) 110 - _40_ = 70
6) 90 - _80_ = 10
7) 40 - _10_ = 30
8) 70 - _50_ = 20
9) 80 - _30_ = 50
10) 150 - _70_ = 80

11) 50 - _10_ = 40
12) 110 - _90_ = 20
13) 160 - _70_ = 90
14) 100 - _90_ = 10
15) 70 - _40_ = 30
16) 140 - _80_ = 60
17) 60 - _30_ = 30
18) 70 - _20_ = 50
19) 70 - _10_ = 60
20) 170 - _80_ = 90

Find the Missing Subtrahends

Fill in the blanks.

1) 120 - _30_ = 90
2) 140 - _60_ = 80
3) 90 - _80_ = 10
4) 110 - _30_ = 80
5) 120 - _50_ = 70
6) 150 - _80_ = 70
7) 140 - _80_ = 60
8) 110 - _80_ = 30
9) 70 - _20_ = 50
10) 90 - _50_ = 40

11) 30 - _20_ = 10
12) 70 - _50_ = 20
13) 100 - _50_ = 50
14) 100 - _10_ = 90
15) 150 - _70_ = 80
16) 40 - _30_ = 10
17) 40 - _10_ = 30
18) 130 - _80_ = 50
19) 100 - _70_ = 30
20) 40 - _20_ = 20

Find the Missing Subtrahends

Fill in the blanks.

1) 40 - _10_ = 30
2) 100 - _10_ = 90
3) 70 - _30_ = 40
4) 150 - _60_ = 90
5) 80 - _70_ = 10
6) 70 - _60_ = 10
7) 100 - _30_ = 70
8) 90 - _40_ = 50
9) 110 - _90_ = 20
10) 40 - _20_ = 20

11) 90 - _50_ = 40
12) 160 - _70_ = 90
13) 110 - _20_ = 90
14) 120 - _80_ = 40
15) 50 - _20_ = 30
16) 120 - _30_ = 90
17) 90 - _60_ = 30
18) 100 - _60_ = 40
19) 90 - _30_ = 60
20) 50 - _30_ = 20

Find the Missing Subtrahends

Fill in the blanks.

1) 60 - _40_ = 20
2) 50 - _10_ = 40
3) 90 - _10_ = 80
4) 160 - _80_ = 80
5) 70 - _50_ = 20
6) 170 - _90_ = 80
7) 140 - _70_ = 70
8) 140 - _80_ = 60
9) 120 - _80_ = 40
10) 100 - _10_ = 90

11) 130 - _60_ = 70
12) 70 - _40_ = 30
13) 100 - _40_ = 60
14) 130 - _70_ = 60
15) 110 - _20_ = 90
16) 140 - _60_ = 80
17) 90 - _50_ = 40
18) 70 - _10_ = 60
19) 160 - _70_ = 90
20) 80 - _60_ = 20

Find the Missing Subtrahends

Fill in the blanks.

1) 110 - _30_ = 80
2) 90 - _60_ = 30
3) 150 - _70_ = 80
4) 70 - _10_ = 60
5) 30 - _10_ = 20
6) 70 - _20_ = 50
7) 130 - _90_ = 40
8) 140 - _60_ = 80
9) 110 - _20_ = 90
10) 140 - _50_ = 90

11) 80 - _10_ = 70
12) 50 - _10_ = 40
13) 60 - _10_ = 50
14) 100 - _20_ = 80
15) 150 - _60_ = 90
16) 100 - _50_ = 50
17) 120 - _40_ = 80
18) 100 - _10_ = 90
19) 80 - _40_ = 40
20) 40 - _30_ = 10

Find the Missing Subtrahends

Fill in the blanks.

1) 70 - _60_ = 10
2) 80 - _50_ = 30
3) 140 - _60_ = 80
4) 160 - _90_ = 70
5) 100 - _80_ = 20
6) 130 - _40_ = 90
7) 70 - _10_ = 60
8) 140 - _70_ = 70
9) 120 - _90_ = 30
10) 60 - _40_ = 20

11) 80 - _10_ = 70
12) 120 - _30_ = 90
13) 120 - _40_ = 80
14) 160 - _80_ = 80
15) 30 - _10_ = 20
16) 120 - _70_ = 50
17) 90 - _10_ = 80
18) 20 - _10_ = 10
19) 90 - _80_ = 10
20) 70 - _50_ = 20

www.claymaze.com

Find the Missing Subtrahends

Fill in the blanks.

1) 80 - _40_ = 40

2) 130 - _70_ = 60

3) 130 - _40_ = 90

4) 110 - _30_ = 80

5) 120 - _60_ = 60

6) 150 - _90_ = 60

7) 80 - _60_ = 20

8) 60 - _30_ = 30

9) 70 - _60_ = 10

10) 150 - _60_ = 90

11) 50 - _20_ = 30

12) 100 - _20_ = 80

13) 110 - _60_ = 50

14) 140 - _80_ = 60

15) 110 - _90_ = 20

16) 70 - _30_ = 40

17) 110 - _40_ = 70

18) 120 - _40_ = 80

19) 100 - _70_ = 30

20) 170 - _90_ = 80